Physical Chemistry

About the Author

Scott L. Kittsley received his doctor's degree in physical chemistry from Western Reserve University in 1945. Since that time he has been associated with Marquette University, where he is now assistant professor of chemistry.

The author has been a contributor to the *Journal of the American Chemical Society* and the *Journal of Chemical Education*. He is a member of the American Chemical Society, the American Association for the Advancement of Science, the Wisconsin Academy of Sciences, Arts, and Letters, and Sigma Xi. He is listed in *American Men of Science* and *Who's Who in American Education*.

PHYSICAL CHEMISTRY

Scott L. Kittsley

BARNES & NOBLE, INC. NEW YORK
PUBLISHERS · BOOKSELLERS · SINCE 1874

©
Copyright 1955
By BARNES & NOBLE, Inc.
All rights reserved
L. C. catalogue card number: 55–6771
Second printing, 1955

Preface

This book summarizes the essentials of an introductory course in physical chemistry. Full-year courses prerequisite to the study of this subject usually include calculus as well as inorganic chemistry, organic chemistry, quantitative analysis, and physics. However, for the benefit of readers who possess only a limited knowledge of calculus, the mathematics in this book does not go beyond the most elementary calculus and, wherever possible, mathematical equations are stated in words.

It is hoped that the book will be of value not only to chemistry majors but also to other students who require a knowledge of the principles of physical chemistry but whose main interests lie in fields such as physics, engineering, biology, biochemistry, and medicine.

Background material necessary for the effective use of this book is available in various other books of the *College Outline Series*. The student will find the following titles especially helpful:

First-Year College Chemistry
Chemistry Problems and How to Solve Them
Physics
College Algebra
The Calculus

In conclusion, the author wishes to thank his wife for her help in critically reading and in typing the manuscript.

Table of Contents

Tabulated Bibliography
of Standard Textbooks

This *College Outline* is keyed to standard textbooks in two ways.

1. If you are studying one of the following textbooks, consult the cross references here listed to find which pages of this *Outline* summarize the appropriate chapter of your text. (Roman numerals refer to the textbook chapters; Arabic figures refer to the corresponding pages of this *Outline*.)

2. If you are using this *Outline* as your basis for study and need a fuller treatment of a topic, consult the pages of any of the standard textbooks as indicated in the Quick Reference Table on pp. xii–xiii.

Amsden, *Physical Chemistry for Premedical Students*, 2nd ed., 1950, McGraw-Hill.
II (3–17); III (18–28); IV (84–85, 95–96); V (62–72); VI (72–73, 114–120, 140–141, 144–146, 159–163); VII (75–79, 133, 138–143); VIII (41–61, 80–84); IX (123–134, 143–144); X (129–132); XI (99–111, 171–174); XII (176–184).

Crockford and Knight, *Fundamentals of Physical Chemistry for Premedical Students*, 1950, Wiley.
I (1–2); II (3–17); III (18–28, 87–88); IV (62–71, 95–96); V (71–72); VI (72–73, 144–147); VII (112–122); VIII (75–80); IX (138–147); X (123–127, 128–132); XI (127–128, 133–134); XII (135–137); XIII (131–132); XIV (99–111); XV (171–175); XVI (176–184); XVII (148–158).

Daniels and Alberty, *Physical Chemistry*, 1955, Wiley.
I (1–2); II (3–17); III (29–35); IV (36–40); V (41–48); VI (48–51); VII (51–57); VIII (18–28, 57–60); IX (62–68); X (68–73); XI (75–84); XII (79–80, 84–85, 86–98); XIII (99–111); XIV (112–122); XV (123–137); XVI (138–147); XVII (171–184); XVIII (148–154); XIX (165–170); XX (154–158).

Eastman and Rollefson, *Physical Chemistry*, 1947, McGraw-Hill.
I (1–2); II (9, 41, 86); III (3, 18, 29, 43, 62); IV (41–46); V (48–51, 162); VI (3–6, 9–12, 43–44, 47–48); VII (6–9, 12–17, 107); VIII (29–35); X (18, 25–27); XI (148–154); XII (159–164); XIII (154–158);

XIV (62–63); XV (51–57, 79, 81–82); XVI (19–20, 57–60, 86–90); XVIII (62–64, 68–72, 84–85); XIX (64–68, 90–96); XX (96–98); XXI (75–84, 138–147); XXII (99–111); XXIII (112–122); XXIV (123–137); XXV (36–37, 38–39, 165–170); XXVI (171–175).

Glasstone, *The Elements of Physical Chemistry*, 1946, Van Nostrand.

I (1–2); II (148–152, 154–158); III (152–154, 159–164); IV (3–17); V (18–28, 36–40, 57–60); VI (29–35, 86–90); VII (41–51); VIII (51–57); IX (69–73); X (75–80); XI (52–53, 80–84); XII (62–67, 90–98); XIII (112–121); XIV (121–122, 123–137); XV (138–141, 144–147); XVI (133–136, 141–144); XVII (171–184); XVIII (99–111); XIX (165–170).

Hammett, *Introduction to the Study of Physical Chemistry*, 1952, McGraw-Hill.

I (3–7); II (7–17); III (62–64); IV (41–44); V (45–51); VI (152–154); VII (51–52, 75–80, 84–85); VIII (52–53, 69–71, 81–84); IX (25–27, 99–111, 169); X (123–137); XI (56–57, 126–127, 128, 134); XII (64–68, 86–98); XIII (112–122, 145–146); XIV (138–147); XV (57–60, 71–72, 128); XVI (24–25, 37–38, 109–110, 171–175).

MacDougall, *Physical Chemistry*, 3rd ed., 1952, Macmillan.

I (1–2); II (41–42, 46); III (3–17, 43–44, 47–48, 107); IV (18–28, 57–60); V (29–35); VI (148–153); VII (152–158, 159–164); VIII (36–40, 167); IX (51–60, 86); X (62–64, 68–72); XI (72–73); XII (48–51); XIII (75–84); XIV (64–67, 84–85, 86–98); XV (99–111, 172–174); XVI (112–122); XVII (138–147); XVIII (123–137); XIX (121–122); XX (165–170); XXI (171–184).

Matsen, Myers, and Hackerman, *Pre-Medical Physical Chemistry*, 1949, Macmillan.

II (148–158); III (159–164); IV (3–6, 12–17); V (6–9, 18, 21–27, 163); VI (29–35); VII (99–111); VIII (75–85); IX (112–122, 144–146); X (21–23, 58–60, 86–90); XI (84–85, 95–96, 144); XII (62–74); XIII (138–143); XIV (123–133); XV (133–137); XVI (135–137); XVII (143–144); XVIII (174–175); XIX (171–174, 175); XX (175–176); XXI (176–180, 182); XXII (180–181); XXIII (181–183).

Millard, *Physical Chemistry for Colleges*, 7th ed., 1953, McGraw-Hill.

I (1–2, 144–145); II (41–46, 51–54); III (48–51); IV (3–17, 20–21, 46–47, 107); V (18–28, 57–60, 175–176); VI (29–35), 171–174); VII (62–72, 84–85); VIII (72–73, 112–122, 126, 145–146); IX (75–79, 82–83, 138–144); X (79–80, 84–85, 144); XI (86–98); XII (99–111); XIII (165–170); XV (154–157); XVI (148–154, 157–158); XVII (176–183); XVIII (54–55, 80–82, 128); XIX (123–137).

Moore, *Physical Chemistry*, 2nd ed., 1955, Prentice-Hall.

I (1–2, 3–9, 18–20, 42, 43–44); II (41–51); III (51–57); IV (52–53, 75–84, 124–126, 128); V (23, 57–60, 86–90); VI (62–73, 84–85, 90–98);

VII (7–9, 12–16, 107, 179–180); VIII (148–152, 154–155); IX (157–158); X (40, 152–154); XI (36–37, 39–40, 159–164); XIII (29–35); XIV (18, 25–27); XV (112–122, 123–137, 138–147); XVI (24–25, 37–38, 171–176, 180–182); XVII (99–111); XVIII (165–170).

Prutton and Maron, *Fundamental Principles of Physical Chemistry*, rev. ed. 1951, Macmillan.

I (3–17); II (41–48, 51–54); III (18–28, 57–60); IV (29–35); V (62–68); VI (68–72); VII (72–73, 144–145); VIII (171–184); IX (48–51); X (51–57); XI (54–57, 81–82); XII (75–79, 80–81, 82–84); XIII (79–80, 84–85); XIV (86–98); XV (112–122); XVI (138–147); XVII (123–137); XVIII (121–122); XIX (99–111); XX (110, 172–174); XXI (148–158); XXII (159–164); XXIII (36–40); XXIV (165–170).

Taylor and Taylor, *Elementary Physical Chemistry*, 3rd ed., 1942, Van Nostrand.

I (148–158); II (41–51, 112, 125–126); III (3–17, 43–44, 46–48, 107); IV (40, 152, 153–154, 179); V (39–40); VI (18–28, 37–38, 58–60, 175–176); VII (29–35, 159–163); VIII (51–60); IX (62–64, 68–73); X (75–85); XI (64–68, 84–85, 86–98); XII (112–122, 145); XIII (138–147); XIV (123–137); XV (99–111, 169); XVI (165–170); XVII (171–184).

Quick Reference Table

Arabic numbers refer to chapters.

See preceding pages

Chapter in This Outline	Topic	Amsden	Crockford & Knight	Daniels & Alberty	Eastman & Rollefson	Glasstone
I	Introduction	*xi*	*1–3*	*1*	*1*	*1–3*
II	The Gaseous State	*2*	*2*	*2*	*62–72* *82–85* *94–97*	*4*
III	The Liquid State	*3*	*35–40* *43–58*	*8*	*160–161* *168–170* *276–282* *485–487*	*127–153*
IV	The Solid State		*12–13*	*3*	*103–126*	*166–178*
V	Physical Properties and Molecular Constitution	*120–122*	*112–113*	*4* *173–174*	*202–203* *467–470*	*157–162*
VI	Elementary Thermodynamics	*8*		*5, 6, 7* *161–167*	*4, 5* *72–75* *249–260*	*7, 8* *139–144* *336–338*
VII	Solutions	*5* *108–110*	*62–73* *75–92* *96–105* *107–111*	*9, 10*	*18* *316–318* *320* *431–432*	*9*
VIII	Chemical Equilibria and Free Energy	*143–149* *193–201*	*8*	*11* *277–281*	*266–268* *346–359*	*10* *324–336* *340–341* *364–367*
IX	The Phase Rule and Phase Equilibria	*64–66*	*40–43* *73–75*	*285–310*	*272–274* *282–285* *320–331* *334–339*	*190–200* *357–360* *371–395*
X	Chemical Kinetics	*254–267*	*14*	*13*	*22*	*18*
XI	Electrolytic Conductance	*129–138*	*7*	*14*	*416–431*	*13* *472–479*
XII	Electromotive Force	*10* *151–152* *203–219*	*10, 11* *13* *262–269*	*15*	*24*	*434–472*
XIII	Ionic Equilibria	*125–128* *140* *152–164* *173–176* *226–236*	*9*	*16*	*359–376*	*15, 16*
XIV	Atomic and Nuclear Structure		*17*	*18, 20*	*11, 13*	*2* *54–62*
XV	Molecular Structure	*117–123*	*111–113*	*55–57* *84–87*	*12*	*62–72*
XVI	Photochemistry			*19*	*473–483*	*19*
XVII	Adsorption and Colloid Chemistry	*12* *267–274*	*15, 16*	*17*	*489–496*	*17*

to Standard Textbooks

Italic numbers refer to pages.

for list of titles.

Hammett	Mac-Dougall	Matsen, Myers, & Hackerman	Millard	Moore	Prutton and Maron	Taylor and Taylor
v-vii	*1-3*	*v-vi*	*1-2*	*1-2*	*1-5*	
1, 2	*28-40* *47-51* *58-68*	4 *64-66*	*80-107* *116-122*	*9-16* *163-171*	*6-44*	*73-100*
27-29 *199-200* *369-370*	4	*66-73*	*126-131* *135-157*	*16-19* *413-432* *501-504*	*77-91* *95-106* *485-488*	*132-141* *154-158*
	102-118	6	*163-184*	*369-383* *392-395*	4	*159-172*
31 *370-371*	*199-208*	*42-44*		*314* *320-321* *326-331*	23	*120* *128-131* *142-143*
4, 5 *157*	2, 12 *42-46* *214-228*		2, 3	2, 3 *19-24* *87-91*	2, 9, 10 *316-321*	*2* *100-101* *184-202* *204-207*
3 *147-152* *264-269* *364-365*	10 *266-274* *375-381* *383-384*	12	*191-200* *205-235* *242-247*	*120-141* *439-442*	6, 7	9 *286-290*
7 *145-147* *158-161*	13 *353-362*	8	*296-315* *336-344* *351-357* *543-564*	*69-72* *74-87*	12, 13 *329-331*	10 *264-271*
254-264 *269-287*	*229-238* *365-375* *384-402*	*133-135* *143-146*	11	*99-105* *109-113* *139-141* *145-155*	14	*272-286* *291-309* *314-318*
166-196 *378-382*	*405-436* *449-472*	7	12	*528-590*	19	*395-405* *418-427* *432-437* *444-454*
292-296 *300-305*	*476-511* *526-527* *652-658* *667-670*	*113-118*	*247-276*	*435-439* *442-447* *488-490*	15	12
10	18	14, 15, 16	19 *330-332*	*473-488*	17, 18	14 *55-56*
316-319 *325-337* *342-345*	17	13, 17	*21* *277-279* *289-292* *315-336* *369-371*	*450-455* *457-465* *469-473*	16	13
	6 *155-178* *182-196*	2	15, 16	8, 9 *251* *259-265*	21	*9-50*
	178-182	3		*295-296* *311-314*	22	*117-118* *167-175*
	20		13	*595-606*	24	16
374-377	21 *437-440*	18, 19, 20, 21, 22, 23	17 *153-156* *185-188*	*498-500* *507-524*	8 *655-657*	17 *440-444*

1

Introduction

Physical chemistry is that branch of chemistry which deals with the study of the physical properties of matter, the structure of matter, and the laws and theories regarding chemical interaction.

Physical chemists seek to codify the data and formulate the basic principles of descriptive chemistry as usually taught in the introductory courses. They have been very successful in many of their attempts to subject chemical behavior to precise mathematical analysis.

This extensive mathematical treatment often proves a stumbling block to the student for two reasons: (1) algebraic rustiness which renders the mechanics of the work discouragingly difficult, and (2) failure to relate the symbols of a mathematical expression to chemical realities. The first difficulty may be overcome by a review of mathematics as related to chemistry.[1] The second difficulty may be met by thorough understanding of each equation as it is presented. Such understanding must go beyond mere memorization of the form of the equation.

Progress in physical chemistry is tested largely by the student's ability to solve specific problems. In problem-solving, the student should first determine what it is he is required to find. Then he should select an equation which contains this quantity and in which he can utilize the other information given in the problem. The more this can be done without reference to the text, the better is the understanding the student has of the subject matter.

For studying the nonmathematical aspects of the subject, the student probably has devised techniques that suit him, and he will find that these may be utilized as well in physical chemistry as in sociology or botany.

[1] For this purpose, two other volumes in the College Outline Series will be found helpful: *Algebra*, by Gerald E. Moore, and *Chemistry Problems and How to Solve Them*, by Paul R. Frey.

1

Although the subject of physical chemistry is admittedly not easy, the student will derive much satisfaction from its study as he begins to understand the laws governing behavior which he had previously accepted and described but which he had been unable to appreciate fully.

2

The Gaseous State

A gas is matter which possesses the property of filling a container completely and to a uniform density. Hence, a gas has neither definite shape nor volume.

The Gas Laws

The gas laws express the effects of temperature and pressure on the volume of a given mass of gas.

Boyle's Law. R. Boyle (1662) discovered that if the temperature remains constant, the volume of a given mass of gas is inversely proportional to the pressure. This law can be represented mathematically as:

$$v \propto \frac{1}{p}, \qquad \qquad 2{:}1$$

in which: $\qquad$ v = volume of gas,

$\qquad$ p = pressure of gas,

$\qquad$ $\propto$ = "is proportional to."

Charles' Law and the Absolute Temperature. Charles' law in its modern form states that if the pressure remains constant, the volume of a given mass of gas is directly proportional to the absolute temperature (represented as degrees K.) or:

$$v \propto T, \qquad \qquad 2{:}2$$

in which T = absolute temperature. The absolute temperature is equal to the centigrade temperature, t, plus 273.16.

The Perfect-Gas Law. Combining equations 2:1 and 2:2:

$$v \propto \frac{T}{p},$$

and converting from a proportionality to an equality by means of a proportionality constant, k:

$$v = \frac{kT}{p} \quad \text{or} \quad pv = kT.$$

3

Note. Since Boyle's law is applicable only at constant temperature and since Charles' law is applicable only at constant pressure, it is not immediately clear that the combination of the two is justified. It follows from these laws that for a given mass of gas the volume is a function of the pressure and the absolute temperature, or:

$$v = f(p, T),$$

and by partial differentiation:

$$dv = \left(\frac{\partial v}{\partial p}\right)_T dp + \left(\frac{\partial v}{\partial T}\right)_p dT.$$

Since for a given mass of gas:

$$v \propto \frac{1}{p} \ (T \text{ constant})$$

or:

$$v = \frac{k_1}{p},$$

then:

$$\left(\frac{\partial v}{\partial p}\right)_T = -\frac{k_1}{p^2} = -\frac{pv}{p^2} = -\frac{v}{p};$$

also since:

$$v \propto T \ (p \text{ constant})$$

or:

$$v = k_2 T,$$

then:

$$\left(\frac{\partial v}{\partial T}\right)_p = k_2 = \frac{v}{T},$$

in which k_1 and k_2 are proportionality constants. Substituting into the expression for dv above:

$$dv = -\frac{v}{p} dp + \frac{v}{T} dT$$

or:

$$\frac{dv}{v} + \frac{dp}{p} = \frac{dT}{T}.$$

Integrating: $\ln v + \ln p = \ln T + \ln$ constant ($\ln$ is the symbol for logarithms to the base e); taking antilogarithms and rearranging: $pv = kT$.

For the special case in which only one mole of gas is considered, $k = R$; R is called the *molar gas constant*. Then:

$$pv = RT \qquad\qquad \textbf{2:3}$$

and for n moles of gas:

$$pv = nRT. \qquad\qquad \textbf{2:4}$$

This last equation is called the *perfect-gas law*.

Evaluation of the Molar Gas Constant. Solving equation 2:3 for R:

$$R = \frac{pv}{T}.$$

R can be shown to have the units of $\dfrac{\text{work}}{\text{degree-mole}}$ in the following manner (remembering that equation 2:3 applies to one mole):

$$R = \frac{pv}{T} = \frac{\left(\dfrac{\text{force}}{\text{area}}\right)\left[(\text{area})(\text{length})\right]}{\text{degree-mole}} = \frac{(\text{force})(\text{length})}{\text{degree-mole}}$$

$$= \frac{\text{work}}{\text{degree-mole}}$$

since: pressure = force per unit area,
          volume = (area)(length),
           work = (force)(distance)   or   (force)(length).

R may be evaluated numerically from the known fact that one mole of any gas at standard conditions (i.e., a pressure of 1 atm. and a temperature of 0° C.) occupies a volume of 22.414 liters. Thus:

$$R = \frac{pv}{T} = \frac{(1\text{ atm.})(22.414\text{ liters})}{273.16\text{ degrees}} = \frac{0.08205\text{ liter-atm.}}{\text{degree-mole}}.$$

This value of R can be used only if the pressure is expressed in atmospheres and the volume is expressed in liters. If other units are used for pressure and volume, R will have other values. Thus, if p is expressed in atm. and v in ml.:

$$R = \frac{(1)(22414)}{273.16} = \frac{82.05\text{ ml.-atm.}}{\text{deg.-mole}}.$$

If R is to be obtained in ergs, p must be expressed in dynes/cm.³ and v in cm.³ A pressure of 1 atm. is the pressure exerted by a column of Hg 76 cm. high and 1 cm.² in cross-sectional area at a temperature of 273.16° K. The volume of such a column is 76.0 cm.³ Since mass equals (density)(volume), the mass of the column is (13.595 g./cm.³)(76.0 cm.³). This quantity is multiplied by the acceleration of gravity (980.66 cm./sec.²) to obtain the force in dynes. Then:

$$R = \frac{pv}{T} = \frac{\left[\dfrac{(13.595\text{ g./cm.}^3)(76.0\text{ cm.}^3)(980.66\text{ cm./sec.}^2)}{\text{cm.}^2}\right]\left[22414\text{ cm.}^3\right]}{273.16\text{ deg.}}$$

$$= \frac{8.314 \times 10^7\text{ g.-cm.}^2}{\text{sec.}^2\text{-deg.-mole}} = \frac{8.314 \times 10^7\text{ ergs}}{\text{deg.-mole}}$$

since: $\dfrac{1\text{ gram} \times 1\text{ cm.}^2}{1\text{ sec.}^2} = 1\text{ erg} = 1\text{ dyne} \times 1\text{ cm.}$

Since 1 joule $= 10^7$ ergs, $R = 8.314$ joules/deg.-mole, and since 1 calorie $= 4.184$ joules:

$$R = \frac{8.314}{4.184} = 1.987 \text{ calories/deg.-mole.}$$

Example. How many liters would 5 moles of H_2 occupy at 25° C. and 2 atm. pressure?

$$pv = nRT.$$

$$v = \frac{nRT}{p}$$

$$= \frac{(5 \text{ moles}) \left(\dfrac{0.0820 \text{ l.-atm.}}{\text{deg.-mole}} \right) (298 \text{ degrees})}{2 \text{ atm.}}$$

$$= 61.1 \text{ liters.}$$

Note. It will be the policy in this book to use exact values for the quantities involved in derivations. However, in order to facilitate calculations by means of a slide rule, data which are accurate to three significant figures will ordinarily be used in the solutions of examples and problems. The approximate values of physical chemical constants are given in the Appendix. Quantities such as 5 moles and 2 atm. may be taken as exact.

Deviations from the Perfect-Gas Law. Gases which obey the simple relationship, $pv = nRT$, are called *perfect gases*. Actual gases show deviations from the perfect-gas law. This is evident from Fig. 1 in

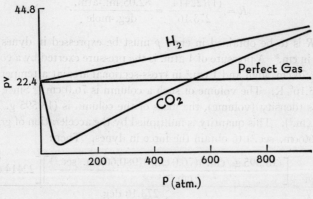

Fig. 1.

which pv at 0° C. for one mole of CO_2 and one mole of H_2 is plotted versus p.

$$pv = nRT = (1)(0.08205)(273) = 22.4 = \text{constant.}$$

Thus, if CO_2 obeyed the perfect-gas law the product pv at 0° C. would equal 22.4 at all pressures. Actually the product pv decreases, passes through a minimum, and then increases until pv is even greater than the expected value of 22.4. For hydrogen, pv is greater than 22.4 at all pressures at 0° C. All gases show a behavior similar to that of CO_2 or H_2 at 0° C. Further, a gas will change from the CO_2 type of deviation to the H_2 type of deviation as the temperature is raised. Note that as the pressure approaches zero the behavior of CO_2 and H_2 (and all other gases) loses its individualistic character and obeys the perfect-gas law.

The minimum in the pv versus p curve for CO_2 indicates that two factors are involved, one of which is predominant at relatively low pressures, whereas the other is predominant at relatively high pressures:

1. At low pressures, the intermolecular attractive forces cause a decrease in the volume, which in turn causes the product pv to be lower than expected.

2. At high pressures, the volume occupied by the molecules is not negligible compared to the total volume; the quantity v in equation 2:3 should represent only the free space available for movement of the molecules, and this is equal to the total volume minus a correction factor for the volume of the molecules. Since this correction is not incorporated in the perfect-gas law, values of pv at high pressures are greater than expected.

Note. H_2 at 0° C. shows such low intermolecular attraction that factor 1 is negligible and, therefore, the gas shows only high values of pv, which are caused by factor 2.

These concepts can be used to modify the perfect-gas law to yield an equation which is better able to predict the behavior of real gases than the relationship $pv = RT$. Van der Waals showed that the corrected or ideal pressure can be represented thus:

$$p + \frac{a}{v^2},$$

in which:
p = actual pressure,
a = constant,
v = volume.

Further, since the molecules occupy some space, the corrected or ideal volume (which represents the volume available for movement of the molecules) is given by:

$$v - b,$$

in which b = constant.

Then, for one mole of gas:

$$\left(p + \frac{a}{v^2}\right)(v - b) = RT. \qquad \textbf{2:5}$$

This equation is known as *van der Waals' equation*. At relatively low pressures, b is negligible compared to v, and van der Waals' equation reduces to:

$$\left(p + \frac{a}{v^2}\right)(v) = RT$$

or:

$$pv = RT - \frac{a}{v},$$

which is in agreement with the observed low values of pv at relatively low pressures for a gas such as CO_2 at $0°$ C.

At relatively high pressures, $\frac{a}{v^2}$ is negligible compared to p, and van der Waals' equation then reduces to:

$$(p)(v - b) = RT$$

or:

$$pv = RT + pb,$$

which is in agreement with the observed high values of pv for CO_2 at $0°$ and high pressures.

At very low pressures (i.e., high volumes) $\frac{a}{v^2}$ approaches zero and b is negligible compared to v. Then van der Waals' equation reduces to $pv = RT$.

Some values for a and b for certain gases are given in the following table:

TABLE 1

Gas	a in atm.-liter²/mole²	b in liters/mole
H_2	0.244	2.66×10^{-2}
He	0.034	2.36×10^{-2}
N_2	1.39	3.91×10^{-2}
CO_2	3.60	4.28×10^{-2}

Van der Waals' equation usually gives much better results than the perfect-gas law, especially at high pressures. For example, one mole of H_2 at $0°$ C. in a volume of 448 ml. shows an observed pressure of 51.6 atm. The pressure calculated from the perfect-gas law is 50 atm. ($- 3.2\%$ deviation). The pressure calculated from van der Waals' equation is 51.75 atm. ($+ 0.02\%$ deviation).

Example. What pressure is required to confine one mole of CO_2 in a volume of 1 liter at 0° C. according to van der Waals' equation?

$$p = \frac{RT}{v - b} - \frac{a}{v^2}$$

$$= \frac{\left(\dfrac{0.0820 \text{ liter-atm.}}{\text{deg.-mole}}\right)(273 \text{ deg.})}{\left[(1 - 0.0428)\dfrac{\text{liter}}{\text{mole}}\right]} - \frac{\dfrac{3.60 \text{ atm.-liter}^2}{\text{moles}^2}}{\dfrac{1^2 \text{ liter}^2}{\text{moles}^2}}$$

$$= 23.4 \text{ atm.} - 3.60 \text{ atm.} = 19.8 \text{ atm.}$$

Note. The units for both terms on the right-hand side of the equation cancel to atmospheres. It is useful to check units in all cases since if they do not cancel to the desired units the problem has been set up incorrectly.

Equations of State. Equations which represent the relationships among the pressure, volume, and temperature of a given mass of a gas are called *equations of state*. Two examples are the perfect-gas law and van der Waals' equation, already discussed. Many other equations of state have been proposed, but most of these merely introduce empirical constants (in addition to a and b).

Molecular Weights of Gases

The perfect-gas law may be used to determine the molecular weight of gases.

Approximate Method. Since, by definition:

$$n = \frac{g}{M},$$

in which:

n = number of moles of gas,
g = grams of gas,
M = molecular weight of gas,

then:

$$pv = nRT = \frac{g}{M} RT, \qquad \qquad \textbf{2:6}$$

and the perfect-gas law can be used to determine molecular weights. Due to deviations of actual gases from the perfect-gas law, the molecular weights obtained are usually 1–2% high at ordinary pressure and temperatures; however, they are sufficiently accurate for use in determining the correct formulas of certain compounds.

Example. Chemical analysis of benzene shows that it contains one atom of carbon to one atom of hydrogen. If 2.58 grams of benzene vapor at 100° C. and 1.00 atm. pressure occupy 1.00 liter, what is the formula of benzene? The atomic weight of carbon is 12.0 and of hydrogen is 1.00.

$$M = \frac{gRT}{pv}$$
$$= \frac{(2.58)(0.0820)(373)}{(1)(1)} = 78.9.$$

Since the molecular weight is about six times the molecular weight corresponding to C_1H_1, the formula for benzene is C_6H_6.

Method of Limiting Densities. Exact molecular weights may be determined by the method of limiting densities. Since:

$$pv = \frac{g}{M} RT,$$

$$M = \frac{g}{v}\frac{RT}{p},$$

but:

$$\frac{g}{v} = d,$$

in which d = density.

Therefore:

$$M = \frac{d}{p} RT. \qquad\qquad 2:7$$

If $\frac{d}{p}$ is plotted versus p, a straight line is usually obtained as in Fig. 2.

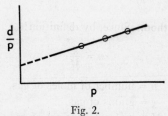

Fig. 2.

The line obtained is extrapolated (extended beyond the range of experimental measurements) to $p = 0$. At $p = 0$, real gases obey the perfect-gas law as shown in Fig. 1. Thus if the extrapolated value of $\frac{d}{p}$ at $p = 0$ is used in equation 2:7, exact molecular weights are obtained. The value $\frac{d}{p}$ at $p = 0$ is given the symbol $\left(\frac{d}{p}\right)_0$. For CH_3Cl, $\left(\frac{d}{p}\right)_0 = 2.2528$. Using values of R and T accurate to five significant figures:

$$M = \left(\frac{d}{p}\right)_0 RT$$

$$= \left(\frac{2.2528 \text{ g.}}{\text{liter-atm.}}\right)\left(\frac{0.082054 \text{ liter-atm.}}{\text{deg.-mole}}\right)(273.16 \text{ deg.})$$

$$= 50.494 \text{ g./mole.}$$

The accepted value based on atomic weights is 50.491 g./mole.

Molecular Weights of Elements. Molecular weight determinations of elements in the gaseous state show that Na, Zn, Hg, and Pb are monatomic (i.e., one atom per molecule). However, at moderate temperatures, hydrogen, nitrogen, oxygen, and the halogens show a molecular weight of twice the atomic weight. Hence their formulas are H_2, N_2, etc. At moderate temperatures, phosphorus exists as P_4 and sulfur as S_8 (an eight-membered ring). As the temperature rises, simplification occurs until at sufficiently high temperatures even these elements become monatomic.

Molecular Association. Some gaseous compounds, instead of showing a molecular weight which corresponds to the usual formula, actually exhibit a molecular weight which is some multiple of the formula weight. For example, acetic acid (CH_3COOH — formula weight = 60) shows a molecular weight of 120 just above its boiling point. This proves that the chemical species involved is really the dimer $(CH_3COOH)_2$. Similarly, just above its boiling point ferric chloride exists as the dimer Fe_2Cl_6. As the temperature increases, these dimers dissociate into the monomers.

Thermal Dissociation. Molecular weights which are abnormally low can be explained on the basis of dissociation. As the temperature is raised, the molecular weight of PCl_5 approaches half the formula value. This is explained by the reaction:

$$PCl_{5g} \rightleftarrows PCl_{3g} + Cl_{2g}.$$

(The subscript g is used for gases, l for liquids, and s for solids.)

Since each molecule of PCl_5 can yield two molecules of products, the actual number of molecules present when the reaction is complete is twice the number that would be present if there were no dissociation. This doubles the volume (at constant pressure) and cuts M in half since $M = \dfrac{gRT}{pv}$.

For a mixture of gases:

$$pv = n_t RT, \qquad \textbf{2:3}$$

in which n_t = total number of moles present.

If n_0 = number of moles of PCl_5 present at start and α = fraction of PCl_5 which is dissociated at equilibrium, then at equilibrium there will be $n_0(1 - \alpha)$ moles of PCl_5, $n_0\alpha$ moles of PCl_3, and $n_0\alpha$ moles of Cl_2 or:

$$n_t = n_0[(1 - \alpha) + \alpha + \alpha] = n_0(1 + \alpha).$$

Then:
$$pv = n_0(1 + \alpha)RT = \frac{g}{M_0}(1 + \alpha)RT, \qquad \textbf{2:9}$$

in which M_0 = molecular weight of PCl_5.

Equation 2:9 is applicable in any case in which one mole of gaseous reactant decomposes into two moles of gaseous products. Two examples are:

$$N_2O_4 \rightleftarrows 2\ NO_2.$$
$$NH_4Cl \rightleftarrows NH_3 + HCl.$$

Other equations can be derived in which other molar ratios are involved.

Example. At 35° C., 4.59 grams of N_2O_4 exerts an equilibrium pressure of 1.60 atmospheres when vaporized in a 1.00-liter flask. Calculate the fraction of N_2O_4 dissociated.

$$M_0 = 92.0.$$

$$pv = \frac{g}{M_0}(1 + \alpha)RT.$$

$$(1.60)(1.00) = \frac{4.59}{92.0}(1 + \alpha)(0.0820)(308).$$

$$1 + \alpha = 1.270.$$
$$\alpha = 0.270 = 27.0\%.$$

Kinetic Theory of Gases

The gas laws and other phenomena may be explained in terms of the kinetic theory of gases.

Derivation of the Kinetic Theory of Gases. The following postulates are provisionally made regarding the ultimate nature of a gas:

1. A gas is composed of minute particles called *molecules*. For any particular gas, all molecules have the same mass and size.

2. The molecules of a gas are in a state of ceaseless, chaotic motion, during which they collide with each other and with the sides of the container.

3. The phenomenon known as pressure is caused by collisions of the molecules with the sides of the container.

4. Collisions between molecules (and between molecules and the sides of the container) must be perfectly elastic (i.e., no kinetic energy is lost due to friction) since the pressure does not decrease with time.

5. At low pressures the molecules are so far apart that the intermolecular attractive forces (which decrease as the distances between the molecules increase) may be considered negligible.

6. At low pressures the volume occupied by the molecules may be considered negligible compared to the volume of the container.

7. The absolute temperature of a gas is a function only of the average kinetic energy of all the molecules.

These concepts may be used to derive a fundamental equation applicable to perfect gases. Consider a cubic vessel with an edge of length l containing one molecule of a gas of mass m which moves with a velocity c; see Fig. 3.

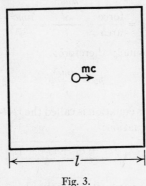

Fig. 3.

The molecule is considered moving toward the right-hand wall of the vessel with a momentum equal to mc. (Momentum = mass × velocity.) It strikes the wall and rebounds. Since the molecule is now moving in the opposite direction, its velocity is now $-c$ and the momentum is $-mc$. Then the change in momentum per collision is $mc - (-mc) = 2mc$.

Since the molecule must travel to the left-hand wall and back before it can collide with the right-hand wall again, it follows that the number of collisions with the right-hand wall per second is $c/2l$, and the change in momentum per molecule per second is:

$$(2mc)\,\frac{c}{2l} = \frac{mc^2}{l}.$$

Now consider the cube to be filled with n molecules. These molecules are moving at random in all directions, but it is possible to regard them as divided into three equal sets: one set moves right and left, another moves up and down, and the third moves in and out (perpendicular to the plane of the page). Thus, of all the molecules in the container, $\frac{n}{3}$ molecules may be considered moving perpendicular to the right-hand face of the cube. Then the change in momentum per $\frac{n}{3}$ molecules per second is $\frac{nmc^2}{3l}$.

According to Newton's laws of motion, the rate of change of momentum is equal to the force acting. Therefore, the force acting on the right-hand face is $\frac{nmc^2}{3l}$. However, since pressure is force per unit area and since the area of a face of a cube is l^2:

$$p = \frac{\text{force}}{\text{area}} = \frac{\dfrac{nmc^2}{3l}}{l^2} = \frac{nmc^2}{3l^3}.$$

But for a cube $l^3 = $ volume; therefore:

$$pv = \frac{nmc^2}{3}. \qquad\qquad \textbf{2:10}$$

The quantity c in this equation is called the *root-mean-square velocity*. It is defined by the equation:

$$c = \sqrt{\frac{c_1^2 + c_2^2 + c_3^2 \cdots c_n^2}{n}},$$

in which:
$c_1 = $ velocity of molecule #1,
$c_2 = $ velocity of molecule #2,
$c_n = $ velocity of molecule #n.

Since the pressure on all faces of the cube is the same, equation 2:10 is general. This equation is called the *fundamental kinetic equation*.

Deductions from the Fundamental Kinetic Equation. Boyle's law and Avogadro's hypothesis may be deduced from the equation.

DEDUCTION OF BOYLE'S LAW. Multiplying numerator and denominator of the fundamental kinetic equation by 2, the following equation is obtained:

$$pv = \frac{2}{3}\left(\frac{nmc^2}{2}\right). \qquad\qquad \textbf{2:11}$$

Since the kinetic energy of a moving molecule is equal to $\frac{1}{2}mc^2$, the quantity in parentheses in equation 2:11 represents the kinetic energy of all the molecules. Further, if the temperature remains constant, the kinetic energy of the molecules remains constant:

$$pv = \tfrac{2}{3}(\text{kinetic energy}) = \tfrac{2}{3}(\text{constant}) = \text{a constant}.$$

This is Boyle's law.

DEDUCTION OF AVOGADRO'S HYPOTHESIS. According to Avogadro's hypothesis, equal volumes of gases under the same conditions of temperature and pressure contain the same number of molecules. Since pressure and volume are equal:

$$p_1 v_1 = p_2 v_2,$$

in which the subscript 1 refers to one gas and the subscript 2 refers to the second gas. Then:

$$\frac{n_1 m_1 c_1{}^2}{3} = \frac{n_2 m_2 c_2{}^2}{3}. \qquad \textbf{2:12}$$

However, since the temperature is constant, the average kinetic energies per molecule must also be equal:

$$\tfrac{1}{2}m_1 c_1{}^2 = \tfrac{1}{2}m_2 c_2{}^2. \qquad \textbf{2:13}$$

Dividing equation 2:12 by equation 2:13:

$$\tfrac{2}{3}n_1 = \tfrac{2}{3}n_2, \quad \text{or} \quad n_1 = n_2.$$

This is a mathematical statement of Avogadro's hypothesis.

The fact that such well-established relationships can be deduced from the fundamental kinetic equation implies that the postulates upon which the fundamental equation is based must be substantially correct. The fundamental kinetic equation is subject to the same restrictions as the perfect-gas law, i.e., it applies exactly only to perfect gases.

Effusion of Gases. Effusion of gas is said to take place when gas passes through a small opening.

Since:
$$pv = \frac{nmc^2}{3},$$

$$c = \sqrt{\frac{3pv}{nm}};$$

but:
$$\text{density} = d = \frac{nm}{v},$$

and:
$$c = \sqrt{\frac{3p}{d}}. \qquad \textbf{2:14}$$

Thus at constant pressure and temperature, the root-mean-square velocity, c, is inversely proportional to the square root of the density. This is a form of *Graham's law*. For two different gases, the root-mean-square velocities are inversely proportional to the square roots of the molecular weights:

$$\frac{c_1}{c_2} = \sqrt{\frac{d_2}{d_1}} = \sqrt{\frac{M_2}{M_1}}, \qquad \text{2:15}$$

since the densities and molecular weights of gases are proportional:

$$\left(M = \frac{dRT}{p} \right).$$

If two different gases (each at the same pressure and temperature) pass through a small aperture, the times, t_1 and t_2, for each gas to pass through are inversely proportional to c:

$$\frac{t_1}{t_2} = \frac{c_2}{c_1} = \sqrt{\frac{M_1}{M_2}} \qquad \text{2:16}$$

Thus equation 2:16 can be used to determine the molecular weight of a gas.

Example. If a liter of O_2 effuses through a small orifice in 60.0 minutes and a liter of He at the same temperature and pressure effuses in 21.2 minutes, what is the atomic weight of He?

$$\frac{t_1}{t_2} = \sqrt{\frac{M_1}{M_2}}.$$

$$\frac{60.0}{21.2} = \sqrt{\frac{32.0}{x}}.$$

$$x = 3.99 = \text{atomic weight of He.}$$

Since:
$$c = \sqrt{\frac{3pv}{nm}} = \sqrt{\frac{3RT}{M}}, \qquad \text{2:17}$$

the root-mean-square velocity can be calculated. In using equation 2:17 it is necessary that R be expressed in ergs/deg.-mole so that c is expressed in cm./sec.

Example. Calculate the root-mean-square velocity of a hydrogen molecule at 25° C.

Step 1. First show that c is obtained in cm./sec. if R is expressed in ergs/deg.-mole.

$$c = \sqrt{\frac{\left(\dfrac{ergs}{deg.\text{-}mole}\right)(deg.)}{\dfrac{g.}{mole}}}$$

$$= \sqrt{\frac{\left(\dfrac{g.\text{-}cm.^2}{sec.^2\text{-}deg.\text{-}mole}\right)(deg.)}{\dfrac{g.}{mole}}}$$

$$= \sqrt{\frac{cm.^2}{sec.^2}} = cm./sec.$$

Step 2. Substitute appropriate values.

$$c = \sqrt{\frac{(3)(8.31 \times 10^7)(298)}{2.02}}$$
$$= 1.92 \times 10^5 \ cm./sec.$$
$$= 1.19 \ miles/sec.$$

Review Questions and Problems

1. State in the form of an equation and give the meaning of each symbol used for (a) Boyle's law; (b) Charles' law; (c) perfect-gas law; (d) fundamental kinetic equation.

2. Derive (a) the perfect-gas law; (b) the fundamental kinetic equation.

3. Determine the value of R in four units commonly used in physical chemistry.

4. What are the two chief causes of the deviations of real gases from ideal or perfect behavior? How are these factors allowed for in van der Waals' equation?

5. Outline a method for determining *exact* molecular weights by means of an application of the perfect-gas law.

Note. The perfect-gas law may be used in the solutions of problems unless otherwise directed.

6. What is the volume of 8.0 grams of H_2 at a pressure of 0.50 atm. and at $0°$ C.?

7. One gram of a certain organic compound gave 200 ml. of vapor at $250°$ C. and 1 atm. pressure. What is the approximate molecular weight of the compound?

8. For a reaction of the type $A_g \rightleftarrows B_g + C_g$ calculate the degree of dissociation if 2.0 grams of A (molecular weight = 60) exert a pressure of 8.40 atm. when vaporized in a 0.5-liter flask at $1000°$ C.

9. Calculate the root-mean-square velocity of an O_2 molecule at $0°$ C.

3

The Liquid State

Liquids are characterized by the fact that they occupy a definite volume which is independent of the volume of the container. Liquids are relatively incompressible compared to gases, and under ordinary circumstances the density of liquids is considerably greater than that of gases. The higher densities of liquids indicate that their molecules are closer together than those of a gas; thus there must be intermolecular attractive forces of high magnitude in the liquid state.

Critical Phenomena in Liquids

Before proceeding with principles governing the liquefaction of gases, certain new concepts must be introduced.

Critical Temperature. If a tube, partially filled with water, is sealed and evacuated, some of the water evaporates to form water vapor (a gas). The resulting system is illustrated in Fig. 4.

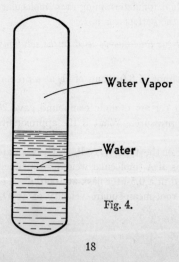

Water Vapor

Water

Fig. 4.

If the tube is now heated, the meniscus (line of demarcation) between the water and water vapor remains until a temperature of 374° C. is reached. At this temperature, the meniscus disappears, the system becomes homogeneous, the densities of the liquid and vapor become equal, and a distinction no longer can be made between liquid and vapor. At temperatures above 374° C. there is no evidence for the presence of liquid no matter how high an external pressure is applied.

The phenomena described above for water are exhibited by all liquids. The *critical temperature* may be defined as the temperature above which it is impossible to liquefy a gas no matter how high the pressure.

Critical Pressure. The pressure exerted by a gas at the critical temperature is called the *critical pressure*.

Critical Volume. The volume occupied by one mole of gas at the critical temperature and pressure is called the *critical volume*.

Application of van der Waals' Equation to Liquids

If van der Waals' equation, 2:5, is multiplied out, and if the result is arranged in descending powers of v, the following equation is obtained:

$$v^3 - \left(\frac{bp + RT}{p}\right)v^2 + \left(\frac{a}{p}\right)v - \frac{ab}{p} = 0. \qquad \textbf{3:1}$$

Since this equation is a cubic equation, there are three values of v for each value of p, if the other quantities are treated as constants. Depending on the values of the constants, either the three values of v obtained may be all real or one may be real and two imaginary.

Each curve in Fig. 5 (p. 20) is a plot of p versus v for a given gas at a constant temperature. These curves are called *isothermals* since each refers to a constant temperature. At T_1 the gas obeys Boyle's law and liquefaction does not occur no matter how high the pressure. The temperature T_1 must therefore be above the critical temperature of the gas in question.

At a lower temperature, T_2, the curve exhibits a discontinuity as shown by the horizontal portion. This indicates that a slight increase in pressure causes a large decrease in volume (due to liquefaction of the gas). The highest temperature at which a horizontal portion of the p-v curve is obtained is the critical temperature of the gas.

At still lower temperatures, T_3 and T_4, the portion of the curve which represents liquefaction is $\sim$-shaped. If p-v determinations

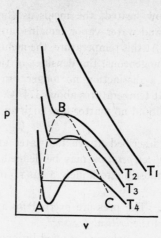

Fig. 5.

are made on actual substances and the results plotted in a similar way, substantially the same curves are obtained. The only essential difference is that the ⌣-shaped portions of the curves are replaced by horizontal lines.

Only within the area ABC (represented by the dotted line) can both the gas and liquid coexist. Outside this area only gas or liquid (but not both) can exist. Thus, van der Waals' equation predicts a critical temperature, T_2, above which it is impossible to liquefy a gas no matter how high the pressure, since at temperatures above T_2 the isothermal curves do not enter the area ABC.

If equation 3:1 is solved at the critical temperature, it is possible to show that:

$$a = 3p_c v_c^2 \quad \text{and} \quad b = \frac{v_c}{3},$$

in which:
p_c = critical pressure,
v_c = critical volume.

This is one way of evaluating the van der Waals' constants.

The Liquefaction of Gases

In order to liquefy gases which have low critical temperatures, the following principles should be borne in mind:

1. The gas must be below its critical temperature before it can be liquefied.

2. The pressure must be high enough to cause liquefaction.

3. A compressed gas is cooled by expansion since, in expanding, energy is required to overcome the intermolecular forces of attraction.

The liquefaction of air is accomplished as follows: At a temperature below the critical temperatures of N_2 and O_2, air is compressed and allowed to expand by passing through a nozzle; in doing so it cools. This cool air is used to cool the incoming compressed air. The cold compressed air in passing through the nozzle is further cooled and liquefies.

Vapor Pressure

If a liquid is placed in a beaker and the beaker is enclosed in a glass vessel at a certain constant temperature, some of the molecules in the surface layer of the liquid evaporate into the free space above. However, some of the molecules of the vapor return to the surface layer of the liquid (i.e., they condense).

Initially the rate of evaporation is large and the rate of condensation is small. As time goes on, the rate of evaporation decreases and the rate of condensation increases until the two rates are equal and the system is in a state of equilibrium. The vapor is then saturated.

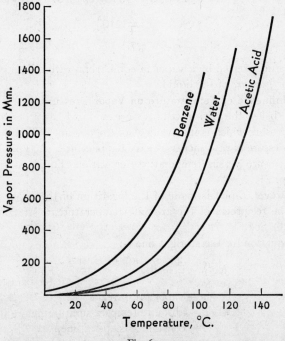

Fig. 6.

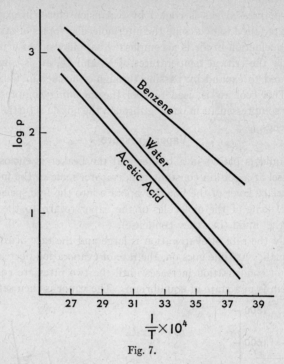

Fig. 7.

The pressure exerted by a vapor in equilibrium with a liquid is called the *vapor pressure* of the liquid.

The Influence of Temperature on Vapor Pressure. At any temperature below the critical temperature, a liquid has a characteristic vapor pressure which is independent of the amount of liquid present. Vapor pressure always increases with temperature. A typical plot of vapor pressure versus temperature for various liquids is shown in Fig. 6 (p. 21).

If, however, a plot is made of the logarithm of the vapor pressure versus the reciprocal of the absolute temperature, a straight line is obtained. See Fig. 7.

The equation for the straight line is:

$$\log p = \frac{A}{T} + B, \qquad\qquad \textbf{3:2}$$

in which:
p = vapor pressure,
T = absolute temperature,
A = constant = slope of line,
B = constant = y-intercept.

Note. Equation 3:2 is similar to $y = mx + b$, which is the equation of a straight line from analytic geometry. In this equation m represents the slope of the line and b represents the y-intercept.

Thus if the vapor pressure is known at two temperatures, the data can be plotted on a log p versus $\frac{1}{T}$ graph, and the vapor pressure at some other temperature can be read off.

Measurement of Vapor Pressure. Vapor pressures may be measured in various ways. The simplest method is to place a little of the liquid above the mercury in the vacuum of a barometer tube and heat to the desired temperature; the depression of the column of mercury is a measure of the vapor pressure.

Empirical Boiling-Point Relationships

It has been found that for many liquids the following relationship is approximately true:

$$\frac{T_b}{T_c} \cong 0.66,$$

in which: T_c = critical temperature in degrees absolute,
T_b = normal boiling point in degrees absolute
(i.e., boiling point at an external pressure of 1 atm.).
(The sign $\cong$ means "is approximately equal to.")
According to Trouton's rule:

$$\frac{L_v}{T_b} \cong 21,$$

in which L_v = molar heat of vaporization in calories (heat required to vaporize one mole of a substance at its boiling point),
T_b = normal boiling point in degrees absolute.
The approximate nature of the relationship is emphasized in Table 2.

TABLE 2

Substance	$\dfrac{T_b}{T_c}$	$\dfrac{L_v}{T_b}$
Oxygen	0.58	17.9
Ammonia	0.59	23.2
Carbon Tetrachloride	0.63	20.4
Water	0.58	26.0
Benzene	0.63	21.2

Nevertheless, these approximate relationships are useful when the value desired is not given in the literature.

Surface Tension

The molecules in the body of a liquid are subject to a balanced intermolecular attractive force exerted by the molecules adjoining them. A molecule in the surface layer, however, is subject to an unbalanced force because there are many other molecules below it, but few above it. Thus, the molecules in the surface layer are pulled inward, and the liquid tends to assume that shape which has the smallest possible surface area (i.e., a sphere). This behavior of the surface of a liquid is called *surface tension*.

Measurement of Surface Tension by Capillary Action. Most liquids (e.g., water) wet the walls of a glass capillary tube; the liquid adhering to the walls pulls the body of the liquid up. This causes liquids which wet the walls to rise in a capillary tube. If the liquid does not wet the walls (e.g., mercury) the liquid is depressed. The best way to measure the surface tension is by measuring the height the liquid rises in a capillary tube of known radius.

A capillary tube of known radius r is immersed in a liquid of density d. Assuming that the liquid wets the walls, the liquid will rise until the force of surface tension which tends to pull the liquid up is just counterbalanced by the force tending to pull the liquid down. The height to which the liquid rises above the surface is represented by h.

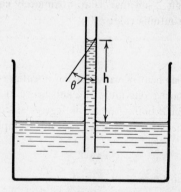

Fig. 8.

The force tending to pull the liquid down is $\pi r^2 h d g$, in which g is the acceleration due to gravity. The force tending to pull the liquid up is $2\pi r \gamma \cos \theta$, in which γ is the surface tension of the liquid and θ is the angle of contact between the surface of the liquid and the walls of the tube. Thus:

$$\pi r^2 hdg = 2\pi r\gamma \cos\theta$$

or:
$$\gamma = \frac{hdgr}{2\cos\theta}.$$

Since $\theta \cong 0$ for most liquids, $\cos\theta = 1$. Then:

$$\gamma = \frac{hdgr}{2}.$$

If h and r are in cm., d in grams/cubic centimeter, and g in $\dfrac{cm.}{sec.^2}$, then

surface tension has the units of $\dfrac{dynes}{cm.}$.

$$\gamma = (cm.)\left(\frac{g.}{cm.^3}\right)\left(\frac{cm.}{sec.^2}\right)(cm.)$$

$$= \left(\frac{g.\text{-}cm.}{sec.^2}\right)\left(\frac{1}{cm.}\right) = \frac{dynes}{cm.}.$$

Example. Acetone rises 5.12 cm. in a capillary tube which has a radius of 0.0117 cm. The density of acetone is 0.790 g./cm.³ Calculate the surface tension of acetone.

$$\gamma = \frac{(5.12)(0.790)(981)(0.0117)}{2}$$

$$= 23.2 \text{ dynes/cm.}$$

Surface Tension and Temperature. The relationship between surface tension and temperature is given by the Ramsay-Shields equation:

$$\gamma\left(\frac{M}{d}\right)^{\frac{2}{3}} = k(T_c - T - 6),$$

in which: γ = surface tension in dynes/cm.,
M = molecular weight,
d = density of liquid in g./cm.³,
k = Eötvös constant = 2.12 for most liquids,
T_c = critical temperature in degrees absolute,
T = absolute temperature of liquid.

The Eötvös constant for water, alcohols, and carboxylic acids is less than 2.12 and varies with the temperature. This is because these liquids form associated molecules in the liquid state. See p. 163.

Viscosity

Liquids flow as if they were divided into layers flowing over one another. Resistance offered to this type of flow is due to friction between the liquid layers and is called *viscosity*. The reciprocal of viscosity is called *fluidity*.

Coefficient of Viscosity. The coefficient of viscosity, η, is defined as:

$$\eta = \frac{df}{Au},$$

in which d = distance between two layers,

   f = force required to maintain a constant difference between the velocities of two parallel layers moving in the same direction,

   u = difference in velocity of the two parallel layers,

   A = area of surface contact of the two layers.

If f is in dynes, d in cm., A in cm.², and u in cm./sec., then η has the units of dynes-sec./cm.² or poises.

$$\eta = \frac{(cm.)(dynes)}{(cm.^2)(cm./sec.)} = \frac{dynes\text{-}sec.}{cm.^2} = poises.$$

Measurement of Viscosity. The viscosity of a liquid can be most conveniently measured by observing the flow of liquid through a capillary. Poiseuille's equation gives the quantitative relationship:

$$\eta = \frac{\pi p r^4 t}{8vl},$$

in which: η = coefficient of viscosity in poises,

   v = volume of liquid which flows through the capillary in cm.³,

   l = length of capillary in cm.,

   r = radius of capillary in cm.,

   t = time of flow in sec.,

   p = driving pressure in dynes/cm.²

However, if the driving pressure is due to the force of gravity:

$$p = hdg,$$

in which: h = height of liquid,

   d = density of liquid,

   g = acceleration due to gravity.

Then:

$$\eta = \frac{\pi r^4 hdgt}{8vl}.$$

If equal volumes of two liquids flow through the same capillary under the same driving pressure:

$$\frac{\eta_1}{\eta_2} = \frac{\left(\frac{\pi r^4 hg}{8vl}\right) d_1 t_1}{\left(\frac{\pi r^4 hg}{8vl}\right) d_2 t_2}$$

or:

$$\frac{\eta_1}{\eta_2} = \frac{d_1 t_1}{d_2 t_2},$$

in which: η_1 = coefficient of viscosity of liquid #1,
η_2 = coefficient of viscosity of liquid #2,
d_1 = density of liquid #1,
d_2 = density of liquid #2,
t_1 = time of flow of liquid #1,
t_2 = time of flow of liquid #2.

Thus if the viscosity of a reference liquid is known, then the viscosity of another liquid can be determined from density and time data.

Example. A certain volume of heptane flows through a capillary in 64.0 sec. at 20° C., while under the same conditions, water requires 108 sec.

$$d \text{ (of } H_2O) = 1.00 \text{ at } 20° \text{ C.,}$$
$$d \text{ (of heptane)} = 0.689 \text{ at } 20° \text{ C.,}$$
$$\eta \text{ (of } H_2O) = 0.0101 \text{ poise.}$$

Calculate the viscosity of heptane.

$$\frac{\eta_1}{0.0101} = \frac{(0.689)\,(64.0)}{(1.00)\,(108)} = 0.00412 \text{ poise.}$$

Influence of Temperature on Viscosity. The viscosity of liquids decreases about 2% for each degree rise in temperature.

Review Questions and Problems

1. Define the critical temperature, pressure, and volume of a gas.

2. Show that the existence of the critical temperature would be expected from van der Waals' equation.

3. Summarize the principles involved in the liquefaction of gases with low boiling points (as air).

4. Acetone has a surface tension of 23.7 dynes/cm. at 20° C. and a density of 0.792 g./cm.^{3}; it rises 1.5 cm. in a certain capillary. What is the radius of the capillary?

5. The vapor pressure of water at 25° C. is 23.8 mm. and at 50° C. is 92.5 mm. With the aid of a log p versus $1/T$ plot, determine the vapor pressure at 40° C. (Actual value = 55.3 mm.)

6. Using the data in Problem 4, calculate the critical temperature of acetone, CH_3COCH_3, assuming the Eötvös constant of acetone is 1.9.

7. A certain volume of water at 20° C. (η = 0.0101 poise and density = 1 g./cm.³) passes through a certain capillary in 100 sec., while an equal volume of another liquid (density = 0.700) passes through in 70 sec. Calculate the viscosity of the liquid.

8. A certain liquid paraffin hydrocarbon (molecular weight = 100) has a boiling point of 80° C. Calculate the approximate critical temperature and approximate heat of vaporization per gram.

4

The Solid State

Solids have a fixed shape and volume. The individual units of a solid (atoms, molecules, or ions) are firmly bound together so that there is little freedom of translational motion. The thermal energy contained in the solid manifests itself mainly in the form of vibrations of the units about a fixed position.

Liquids may solidify as either amorphous or crystalline solids. Amorphous solids (as glass) may be regarded as supercooled liquids of very high viscosity. Amorphous solids show an indefinite melting point and have rather indefinite arrangements of the structural units. Crystalline solids exhibit a regularity in the arrangement of the structural units and a sharp melting point.

Crystals whose properties (e.g., refractive indices) are different along different axes of the crystal are called *anisotropic*. If the properties are the same in all directions the crystal is said to be *isotropic*. If anisotropic crystals are viewed with polarized light, characteristic color patterns are obtained. These are useful in identification.

Crystal Forms

Crystallography is the study of the geometry, structure, and properties of crystals.

Crystal Systems. All crystals belong to one of the following six crystal systems:

1. *Cubic*. Three axes of equal length intersecting each other at right angles.

2. *Tetragonal*. Three axes all intersecting each other at right angles, with only two of the axes equal in length.

3. *Hexagonal*. Three axes of equal length in a single plane all intersecting at 60° angles, and a fourth axis of different length and perpendicular to the plane of the other three.

4. *Rhombic*. Three axes of unequal length all intersecting at right angles.

5. *Monoclinic.* Three axes of unequal length, two of which intersect at right angles.

6. *Triclinic.* Three axes of unequal length, none of which intersect
at right angles. See Fig. 9.

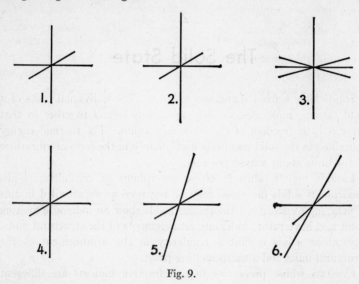

Fig. 9.

Miller Indices. The position of a plane in space can be represented
by three points in a system of co-ordinates, i.e., X, Y, and Z. It is
possible to determine the face of a crystal by noting its points of intersection with the three axes. However, in crystallography crystal
faces are usually defined in terms of the Miller indices. If unit
distances along the X, Y, and Z axes are called a, b, and c respectively,
the Miller indices are the reciprocals of the intercepts expressed as a
ratio of small whole numbers. (If a plane is parallel to an axis, it
cuts that axis at infinity and the Miller index is zero.) For example,
if a plane cuts the X, Y, and Z axes at 2, 1, and $\frac{1}{2}$ respectively, the
reciprocals are $\frac{1}{2}$, 1, and 2 respectively and the Miller indices are
1, 2, and 4.

The Structure of Cubic Crystals. There are three possible arrangements or space lattices in the cubic system. They are:

1. *Simple Cubic Lattice.* One structural unit at each corner of the
cube.

2. *Face-centered Cubic Lattice.* One unit at each corner of the cube
and one unit in the center of each face of the cube.

3. *Body-centered Cubic Lattice.* One unit at each corner of the cube and one unit in the center of the cube.

Planes which cut the X-axis at a or some integral multiple of a and which are parallel to the Y- and Z-axes have Miller indices of one, zero, zero; such planes are called 100 planes. Planes which cut the X- and Y-axes at a or some integral multiple of a and which are parallel to the Z-axis have Miller indices of one, one, zero; such planes are called 110 planes. Planes which cut the X-, Y-, and Z-axes at a or some integral multiple of a have Miller indices of one, one, one; such planes are called 111 planes.

The notations d_{100}, d_{110}, d_{111} indicate the distances between two adjacent 100, 110, and 111 planes, respectively. This is seen more clearly in Fig. 10, which represents the 100, 110, and 111 planes in a simple cubic lattice.

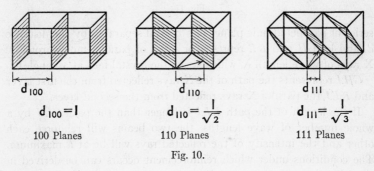

d_{100}	d_{110}	d_{111}
$d_{100} = 1$	$d_{110} = \dfrac{1}{\sqrt{2}}$	$d_{111} = \dfrac{1}{\sqrt{3}}$
100 Planes	110 Planes	111 Planes

Fig. 10.

On the basis of geometrical arguments it can be shown that the ratio of $d_{100} : d_{110} : d_{111}$ is characteristic for the several cubic lattices. They are:

LATTICE TYPE	d_{100}:	d_{110} :	d_{111}
Simple cubic	1 :	(0.707) :	(0.578)
Face-centered cubic	1 :	(0.707) :	(1.155)
Body-centered cubic	1 :	(1.414) :	(0.578)

X Rays and Crystal Structure

X rays may be used to determine the lattice type of a crystal.

Laue Method. X rays are radiant energy with wave lengths of about 10^{-8} cm. or 1 angstrom. If a beam of X rays is directed at a crystal and a photographic plate is placed behind the crystal, a characteristic pattern is obtained upon development of the photographic plate, since the crystal acts as a three-dimensional diffraction grating. From such a pattern, it is possible to elucidate the geometry of the structural units of the crystal although the mathematical analysis is quite complex. The method is called the *Laue* or *transmission method*.

Bragg Method. The *Bragg* or *reflection method* gives results which are easier to interpret. In Fig. 11 let *AB*, *CD*, and *EF* represent a

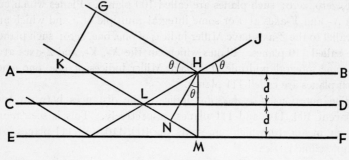

Fig. 11.

series of parallel atomic planes of a crystal separated by the distance *d*, and let *GH* and *KL* represent a series of parallel monochromatic X rays of wave length λ, which strike the crystal face at an angle θ.

GHJ represents the path of the X rays reflected from the first layer and *KLJ* the path of X rays reflected from the second layer.

If the length of the path *KLJ* is longer than the path *GHJ* by a whole number of wave lengths, the two beams will reinforce each other and the intensity of the reflected rays will be at a maximum. The conditions under which reinforcement occurs can be derived in the following manner.

The line *HM* is drawn perpendicular to *AB*, and *HN* is drawn perpendicular to *LM*. It follows from the geometry of the diagram that the angles marked θ are equal, that *LH* = *LM*, and that the path *KLJ* is longer than the path *GHJ* by an amount, *l*, which is equal to *LH* − *LN*. Since:

$$LH = LM,$$
$$l = LH - LN = LM - LN = NM.$$

But:
$$\sin \text{ angle } NHM = \sin \theta = \frac{NM}{HM}$$

or $NM = HM \sin \theta$; but since $l = NM$ and $HM = 2d$:
$$l = 2d \sin \theta.$$

For a reflection of maximum intensity, *l* must be a whole number of wave lengths, or:
$$n\lambda = 2d \sin \theta, \qquad \textbf{4:1}$$

in which n is a whole number called the *order of reflection*. If n, λ, and θ are known, the distance, d, between two atomic planes can be calculated by using equation 4:1.

Example. A sodium chloride crystal gives first-order reflection maxima at 5.9°, 8.4°, and 5.2° for the d_{100}, d_{110}, and d_{111} planes respectively. What is the type of cubic lattice?

$$n\lambda = 2d \sin \theta \quad \text{or} \quad d = \frac{n\lambda}{2 \sin \theta}.$$

For first-order reflection $n = 1$, and:

$$d = \frac{\lambda}{2 \sin \theta}.$$

$$d_{100} = \frac{\lambda}{2(0.103)}.$$

$$d_{110} = \frac{\lambda}{2(0.146)}.$$

$$d_{111} = \frac{\lambda}{2(0.0906)}.$$

Since $\dfrac{\lambda}{2}$ is the same for the three cases:

$$d_{100}:d_{110}:d_{111} = \frac{1}{0.103} : \frac{1}{0.146} : \frac{1}{0.0906}$$

$$= 1:(0.705):(1.14).$$

Therefore the crystal is of the face-centered cubic type.

Crystal Structure of Sodium Chloride

The crystal structure of sodium chloride consists of a face-centered cubic lattice of sodium ions interlocked with a similar lattice of chloride ions as shown in Fig. 12.

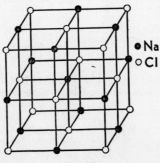

●Na
○Cl

Fig. 12.

It is evident that each sodium ion is surrounded by six chloride ions and vice versa. There is no such entity as a sodium chloride molecule since no one sodium ion can be said to belong to any particular chloride ion. Other substances which have a structure similar to that of NaCl include MgO, CaO, and PbS.

Calculation of the Wave Length of X Rays

It is possible to use equation 4:1 to calculate the wave length of X rays. For example, with X rays of a certain wave length, the first-order reflection from the d_{100} planes of NaCl occurs at 5.9°. NaCl has a face-centered cubic lattice, a molecular weight of 58.5, and a density of 2.17.

A crystal may be considered to be built up by the repetition of a three-dimensional basic pattern. This basic pattern is called the *unit cell*. A unit cell represents the simplest structure that contains one unique ion. The unit cell of NaCl is represented by Fig. 12. In this unit cell there are 13 sodium ions and 14 chloride ions. There is one chloride ion at each corner of the cube (a total of 8) and one chloride ion in the center of each face (a total of 6). However, those at the corners of the cube are shared with 7 other unit cells, so only $\frac{1}{8}$ of 8 or 1 chloride ion belongs to the cell under consideration. The 6 chloride ions in the center of each face are shared between two unit cells, giving only 3 per cell. Thus there are $3 + 1 = 4$ chloride ions associated with each unit cell.

Of the 13 sodium ions, the one in the center belongs completely to the cell in question, but the remaining 12 are shared with 3 other unit cells. Thus the sodium ions belonging to the cell in question number $1 + \frac{1}{4}(12) = 4$.

One unit cell, therefore, contains 4 sodium ions and 4 chloride ions or 4 sodium chloride "molecules." Further, the molar volume, MV, is:

$$MV = \frac{\text{molecular weight}}{\text{density}} = \frac{58.5}{2.17} = 27.0 \text{ cm.}^3$$

But this is the volume occupied by one mole or 6.02×10^{23} molecules. The volume, V, which is occupied by 4 molecules (or the volume of the unit cell) is:

$$V = \frac{4(27.0)}{6.02 \times 10^{23}} \text{ cm.}^3$$
$$= 179 \times 10^{-24} \text{ cm.}^3$$

The length of an edge of the unit cell is the cube root of V or 5.63×10^{-8} cm. Since d_{100} is $\frac{1}{2}$ the length of the edge of the unit cell (Fig. 12):

$$d_{100} = \tfrac{1}{2}(5.63 \times 10^{-8}) = 2.82 \times 10^{-8} = 2.82 \text{ Å}.$$

Since: $$n\lambda = 2d \sin \theta \quad \text{and} \quad \lambda = \frac{2d \sin \theta}{n}:$$

$$\lambda = \frac{(2)(2.82 \times 10^{-8})(\sin 5.9°)}{1}$$

$$= 0.581 \text{ Å}.$$

Results of X-Ray Investigation

The geometry and nature of the structural units have been determined for a large number of crystals. For example, diamond consists of carbon atoms tetrahedrally linked, i.e., every carbon atom is bound to four other atoms each of which is situated at the corners of a tetrahedron. The distance between any two adjoining atoms is 1.54 Å. The carbon atoms in graphite are arranged in flat, parallel layers which are 3.41 Å. apart. In each layer the atoms are arranged in the form of hexagons in which adjoining atoms are 1.40 Å. apart. Graphite can be used as a lubricant since one layer of atoms easily slides over another.

Review Questions and Problems

1. Define the six crystal systems.
2. What are the Miller indices of a crystal face?
3. Derive $n\lambda = 2d \sin \theta$.
4. The first-order reflection of a beam of X rays from the d_{100} planes of a NaCl crystal occurs at 6.1°. What is the wave length of the X rays? Sin 6.1° = 0.106.
5. In the reflection of X rays of $\lambda = 0.580$ Å., the second-order maxima from the d_{100}, d_{110}, and d_{111} planes are obtained at $\theta = 11.9°$, 17.0°, and 10.5° respectively. What type of lattice does this crystal have?

5

Physical Properties and Molecular Constitution

An *additive property*, e.g., molecular weight, depends on the number and kind of atoms in the molecule.

A *constitutive property*, e.g., the optical rotation of polarized light, depends on the arrangement of atoms within the molecule.

A *colligative property*, e.g., the pressure of a gas, depends only on the number of atoms or molecules present.

Many physical properties are partly additive and partly constitutive, e.g., molar refraction and parachor.

Molar Refraction

The molar refraction, R_m, of a substance is defined by the equation:

$$R_m = \frac{M}{d} \frac{n^2 - 1}{n^2 + 2},$$
5:1

in which:
R_m = the molar refraction,
M = molecular weight,
d = density,
n = refractive index.

The molar refraction is independent of temperature and pressure. The molar refraction depends on the wave length of the light used. In this chapter it is assumed that the D-line of sodium is the light source.

Molar Refraction as an Additive and Constitutive Property. The molar refraction can be determined by adding the appropriate atomic and constitutive refractions. For example, the refraction associated with a CH_2 group is equal to:

$$R_m \text{ of } n\text{-}C_7H_{16} - R_m \text{ of } n\text{-}C_6H_{14}.$$

The atomic refraction of a hydrogen atom is equal to:

$$\frac{R_m \text{ of } n\text{-}C_6H_{14} - 6(R_m \text{ of } CH_2)}{2}.$$

Then the atomic refraction of carbon is R_m of a CH_2 group minus twice the atomic refraction of a hydrogen atom. Table 3 contains various atomic and constitutive refractions.

TABLE 3

ATOMIC AND CONSTITUTIVE REFRACTIONS

C	2.42	Double bond in C = C	1.73
H	1.10	Triple bond in C ≡ C	2.40
Cl	5.97	Carbonyl oxygen	2.21
Br	8.87	Hydroxyl oxygen	1.53
I	13.90	Ether oxygen	1.64

Esters ($R-\overset{\displaystyle O}{\overset{\displaystyle \|}{C}}-O-R$) contain one carbonyl oxygen and one ether oxygen.

Example. For ethyl acetate at 20° C., $n = 1.37$, $d = 0.901$, $M = 88.1$. Calculate R_m using equation 5:1 and the data in Table 3.

From equation 5:1:

$$R_m = \frac{M}{d}\frac{n^2-1}{n^2+2} = \frac{(88.1)\left[(1.37)^2-1\right]}{(0.901)\left[(1.37)^2+2\right]}$$

$$= \frac{(88.1)(1.88-1)}{(0.901)(1.88+2)}$$

$$= 22.2.$$

From data in Table 3:

1 carbonyl oxygen	2.21
1 ether oxygen	1.64
4 C's (4 × 2.42)	9.68
8 H's (8 × 1.10)	8.80
	22.33

Applications of Molar Refraction to Molecular Structure. Molar refractions may be used to decide between alternative structures of organic compounds. The formula accepted is the one giving a value of R_m as calculated from data in Table 3 which is in best agreement with the experimental value of R_m.

The Parachor

The parachor is defined by the equation:

$$P = \frac{M}{D-d}\gamma^{\frac{1}{4}}, \tag{5:2}$$

in which: P = parachor,

M = molecular weight,

D = density of liquid,

d = density of vapor,

γ = surface tension in dynes/cm.

Since d is negligible compared to D, it is usually neglected, and:

$$P = \frac{M}{D}\gamma^{\frac{1}{4}}. \qquad\qquad \textbf{5:3}$$

The parachor is independent of temperature.

Just as R_m is the sum of atomic and constitutive refractions, P is the sum of atomic and constitutive parachors.   See Table 4.

TABLE 4

ATOMIC AND STRUCTURAL PARACHORS

C	4.8	Cl	53.8	Double bond in C=C	23.2
H	17.1	Br	68.0	Triple bond in C≡C	46.6
O	20.0	I	91.0	Six-membered ring	6.1

Example. Calculate P for benzene from equation 5:3 and also by using the data in Table 4, if:

D = 0.879 g./ml. at 20° C.,

M = 78.1,

γ = 28.9 dynes/cm. at 20° C.

$P = \dfrac{78.1}{0.879}(28.9)^{\frac{1}{4}} = 206.$

$$
\begin{array}{lr}
P = (6 \times 4.8) \text{ for carbon} & 28.8 \\
(6 \times 17.1) \text{ for hydrogen} & 102.6 \\
(3 \times 23.2) \text{ double bond} & 69.6 \\
\text{six-membered ring} & \underline{6.1} \\
P = & 207.1
\end{array}
$$

Optical Rotation

When certain substances are placed in the path of a beam of polarized light, the beam is rotated either to the left or to the right.   Such substances are *optically active*.   If the beam is rotated to the right, the substance is *dextrorotatory*.   If the beam is rotated to the left, the substance is *levorotatory*.   The angle of rotation can be measured in a polarimeter.

Optical activity is most commonly found in substances which contain one or more asymmetric carbon atoms (i.e., a carbon atom to

which four different atoms or groups of atoms are attached). The
specific rotation of a substance is defined by:

$$[\alpha]^t_\lambda = \frac{\alpha}{l(g/v)},$$

in which: $[\alpha]^t_\lambda$ = the specific rotation for light of wave
length λ at temperature t,

α = observed rotation in degrees,

l = length of polarimeter cell in decimeters,

g/v = number of grams of optically active
material in v milliliters.

For liquids and solids g/v = density. For solutions g/v represents
the concentration of optically active material.

Example. At 25° C. and using the D-line of Na, an aqueous solution of
maltose containing 13.0 grams in 100 ml. was examined in a polarimeter
cell 1.00 decimeter in length. It was found to have a rotation of 17.0°.
Calculate the specific rotation of maltose. Another solution gave a rotation of 45.0° under the same conditions. What was the concentration in
g./liter of this solution?

$$[\alpha]^{25°\,C.}_D = \frac{17}{(1)(13/100)} = 131°.$$

$$g = \frac{\alpha v}{[\alpha]^{D°\,C.}_{25}l}.$$

$$= \frac{(45)(1000)}{(131)(1)} = 344 \text{ g./l.}$$

The Dipole Moment

Polar molecules are electrically dissymmetrical and can be represented thus $(\;+\;-\;)$, which indicates that there is a finite difference
between the centers of gravity of the positive and negative charges;
polar molecules form nonideal gases. Nonpolar molecules are electrically symmetrical and form nearly perfect gases.

The dipole moment, μ, is a measure of the electrical dissymmetry
of a molecule and is defined as the product of one of the charges and
the distance between the two centers of gravity.

The angles between atoms in a molecule can be determined from
the dipole moment. For example, CO_2 must have one of three
arrangements:

1. symmetrical and linear

2. triangular

3. unsymmetrical and linear

The dipole moment of CO_2 is zero. If CO_2 were unsymmetrical and linear or triangular, there would be unbalanced electrical charges and a finite dipole moment. Hence, CO_2 must have a linear symmetrical structure. The dipole moment of water (combined with other evidence) indicates it has a triangular structure of the type

in which the angle H—O—H is 105°.

Electron Diffraction

Electrons exhibit not only properties associated with particles, but also properties associated with waves (e.g., diffraction). If a beam of electrons passes through a stream of vapor of a substance under investigation and then strikes a photographic plate, development of the plate reveals an electron-diffraction pattern from which it is possible to deduce the positions of the atoms in the molecule and the distances between them.

Review Questions and Problems

1. Define: (a) additive property; (b) constitutive property; (c) colligative property; (d) molar refraction; (e) parachor; (f) dipole moment; (g) specific rotation.

2. Explain why CO_2 must be symmetrical and linear.

3. Calculate the surface tension of p-chorotoluene, $CH_3C_6H_4Cl$, at 25° C. using the data in Table 4; $D = 1.07$, $M = 126.5$.

4. Calculate the molar refraction of acetone using the data in Table 3. Experimental value using equation 5:1 is 16.2.

5. At 25° C. and using the D-line of Na, a certain solution of maltose showed an angle of rotation of 60.0° in a polarimeter tube 2.00 decimeters long. Calculate the concentration of maltose in g./l.

6

Elementary Thermodynamics

Thermodynamics is a study of the quantitative relationships between heat and other forms of energy. Energy is the capacity to do work. Energy (e.g., mechanical energy expressed in ergs) can be considered to be the product of an intensity factor (force in dynes) and a capacity factor (distance in cm.).

First Law of Thermodynamics

The first law of thermodynamics states that energy can be neither created nor destroyed. A system is that part of the universe chosen for consideration. A system at a given temperature which contains a definite amount of mass has a definite internal energy; this energy is a result of the motion of the molecules, the position of the molecules, intermolecular attraction, and other factors. The absolute internal energy of a system is not ascertainable. However, a change in internal energy for a given change in the system is both definite and ascertainable.

$$\Delta E = E_2 - E_1,$$

in which ΔE = change in internal energy,

E_2 = internal energy of system in the final state,

E_1 = internal energy of system in the initial state.

The subscripts 1 and 2 are ordinarily used to indicate the initial and final states respectively.

ΔE depends only on the initial and final states of the system and is independent of the particular path linking the initial and final states. This can be shown from the following. Consider:

state 1 to state 2 by path I,
state 2 to state 1 by path II.

If the energy liberated in path I were greater than that consumed in path II, energy would be created. This is a violation of the first

41

law, and hence ΔE must depend only on the initial and final states of the system.

If heat (q) is added to a system, it will either raise the internal energy, or be converted into work (w) done by the system against the surroundings, or both. From the first law it follows that:

$$\Delta E = q - w, \qquad\qquad 6:1$$

which is a mathematical expression of the first law. If the system absorbs heat from the surroundings, q is positive. If work is done by the system against the surroundings, w is positive. The quantities q and w depend on the path taken between states 1 and 2.

A cyclic process is one in which the final and initial states of the system are identical.

Work of the Pressure-Volume Type

In this chapter the only type of work to be considered is that which is the result of expansion or compression of a gas against an opposing pressure, p. A cylinder of cross-sectional area A is fitted with a frictionless and weightless piston. A gas is enclosed within the cylinder and is allowed to expand against the opposing pressure, p. See Fig. 13.

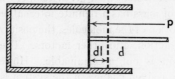

Fig. 13.

The piston is forced to the right an infinitesimal amount dl. The work associated with such a change is:

$$dw = f\, dl,$$

since work is force × distance. However, since force is pressure × area, then:

$$dw = pA\, dl.$$

But $A\, dl$ is the element of volume, dv, swept out by the piston during the expansion. Therefore:

$$dw = pdv$$

or integrating between the limits v_1 and v_2:

$$w = \int_{v_1}^{v_2} pdv. \qquad\qquad 6:2$$

If the opposing pressure is constant:

$$w = p \int_{v_1}^{v_2} dv = p(v_2 - v_1) = p\Delta v. \qquad\qquad 6:3$$

Reversible Processes

A reversible process is one in which the opposing force is infinitesimally smaller than the driving force. Such a process can be reversed by an infinitesimal increase in the opposing force. An example is the vaporization of water at 100° C. and a pressure of 1 atm. If the temperature is raised an infinitesimal amount above 100° C. the water will boil, whereas if the temperature is infinitesimally less than 100° C. the steam will condense. If the pressure is infinitesimally less than 1 atm. the water will boil, whereas if the pressure is infinitesimally greater than 1 atm. the steam will condense. Thus the process is reversible since it can be reversed from boiling to condensation by an infinitesimal change in the temperature or pressure.

Example. One mole of water is vaporized at 100° C. and 1 atm. pressure. The heat of vaporization of water is 9720 cal./mol. Calculate q, w, and ΔE.

$$q = 9720 \text{ cal./mol.}$$
$$w = p(v_2 - v_1).$$

Since $v_2 =$ volume of 1 mole of steam at 100° C.:

$$v_2 = \frac{nRT}{p} = \frac{(1)(0.0820)(373)}{(1)} = 30.6 \text{ l.}$$

and since 1 mole of water occupies about 0.018 l., it is clear that $v_2 - v_1 \cong v_2$, and:

$$w = p(v_2 - v_1) \cong pv_2 \cong RT$$
$$= (1.99)(373) = 742 \text{ cal.}$$

Assuming that steam at 100° C. behaves as a perfect gas:

$$\Delta E = q - w = 9720 - 742 = 8978 \text{ cal.}$$

Maximum Work by Isothermal and Reversible Expansion of a Perfect Gas

From equation 6:2, it is clear that the greater the value of p (the opposing pressure), the greater the value of w. The highest value of p compatible with an expansion is a value just infinitesimally less than the driving pressure. If this is the case, the process must be a reversible one. Thus, it follows that maximum work, $w_{max.}$, is obtained in a reversible process.

In order to expand a gas under reversible conditions, the opposing pressure must readjust itself continuously so as to be less than the pressure of the gas by an infinitesimal amount. See Fig. 14. Then:

$$w_{max.} = \int_{v_1}^{v_2} (p - dp)\, dv = \int_{v_1}^{v_2} pdv - dp\, dv.$$

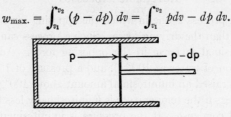

Fig. 14.

Neglecting the small product $dp\, dv$:

$$w_{max.} = \int_{v_1}^{v_2} pdv.$$

If the gas undergoing the expansion is a perfect gas and if the process is isothermal (i.e., takes place at constant temperature) and reversible, $\dfrac{nRT}{v}$ can be substituted for p, and:

$$w_{max.} = nRT \int_{v_1}^{v_2} \frac{dv}{v} = nRT \ln \frac{v_2}{v_1} = 2.303\, nRT \log \frac{v_2}{v_1}, \qquad \textbf{6:4}$$

in which "ln" means logarithm to the base e and "log" means logarithm to the base 10. From Boyle's law:

$$w_{max.} = 2.303\, nRT \log \frac{p_1}{p_2}. \qquad \textbf{6:5}$$

Example. Calculate the work done when 1 mole of He expands from a volume of 1 liter to a volume of 10 liters at 25° C. against a constant opposing pressure of 1 atm. 1 l.-atm. = 24.2 cal.

$$w = p(v_2 - v_1) = (1)(10 - 1) = 9 \text{ l.-atm.}$$
$$w = (9)(24.2) = 218 \text{ cal.}$$

Example. Calculate the work done when 1 mole of He expands isothermally and reversibly from a volume of 1 liter to a volume of 10 liters at 25° C.

$$w_{max.} = 2.30\, nRT \log \frac{v_2}{v_1}$$

$$= (2.30)(1)(1.99)(298) \log \frac{10}{1}$$

$$= 1360 \text{ cal.}$$

Although the initial and final states are the same in the two examples above, w is different because w depends on the path taken between the initial and final states, in contrast to ΔE which is independent of the path. The quantity q is similar to w in this respect.

Heat Changes at Constant Volume
and Constant Pressure

Since: $$w = \int_{v_1}^{v} p \, dv,$$

then: $$\Delta E = q - \int_{v_1}^{v_2} p \, dv$$

if the only work involved is of the pressure-volume type. If the process is conducted at constant volume, dv is 0 and:

$$\Delta E = q_v \qquad \qquad \textbf{6:6}$$

or the heat absorbed in a constant-volume process is equal to the increase in internal energy.

Note. The property indicated by the subscript is kept constant. Thus, q_v indicates that the process under consideration is a constant-volume process.

Most chemical operations are conducted at constant pressure. Then:

$$\Delta E = q_p - w = q_p - p\Delta v. \qquad \textbf{6:7}$$

$$q_p = \Delta E + p\Delta v = (E_2 - E_1) + (pv_2 - pv_1)$$
$$= (E_2 + pv_2) - (E_1 + pv_1).$$

$E + pv$ is an important quantity called *heat content* or *enthalpy* which is given the symbol H:

$$H = E + pv. \qquad \textbf{6:8}$$

Then: $$q_p = H_2 - H_1 = \Delta H \qquad \textbf{6:9}$$

or the heat absorbed in a constant-pressure process is equal to the increase in heat content. ΔH like ΔE depends only on the initial and final states of the system.

Combining equations 6:7 and 6:9:

$$\Delta E = \Delta H - p\Delta v,$$

$$\Delta H = \Delta E + p\Delta v, \qquad \textbf{6:10}$$

or: $$q_p = q_v + p\Delta v. \qquad \textbf{6:11}$$

Thus the heat absorbed in a constant-pressure process exceeds the heat absorbed for the same process at constant volume by the quantity $p\Delta v$. Since:

$$pv_2 = n_2RT \quad \text{and} \quad pv_1 = n_1RT,$$

then:

$$pv_2 - pv_1 = n_2RT - n_1RT = p(v_2 - v_1) = (n_2 - n_1)RT,$$

and:

$$p\Delta v = \Delta nRT.$$

It follows that:

$$q_p = q_v + \Delta nRT. \qquad 6:12$$

Equation 6:12 can be applied to a chemical reaction in which Δn is the number of moles of gaseous products minus the number of moles of gaseous reactants.

Example. For the reaction at 25° C.:

$$Fe_{(s)} + H_2SO_{4(l)} \rightarrow FeSO_{4(s)} + H_{2(g)}$$

calculate $q_p - q_v$. The subscripts s, l, and g indicate solid, liquid, and gas respectively.

$$q_p - q_v = \Delta nRT = (1)(1.99)(298)$$
$$= 593 \text{ cal.}$$

Heat Capacity

The heat capacity of a system, c, is the heat required to raise the temperature of the system 1° C. At constant volume:

$$c_v = \frac{q_v}{T_2 - T_1} = \frac{E_2 - E_1}{T_2 - T_1} = \frac{\Delta E}{\Delta T}. \qquad 6:13$$

At constant pressure:

$$c_p = \frac{q_p}{T_2 - T_1} = \frac{H_2 - H_1}{T_2 - T_1} = \frac{\Delta H}{\Delta T}. \qquad 6:14$$

Since heat capacity varies with temperature, infinitesimally small temperature intervals should be considered. Then:

$$c_v = \left(\frac{\partial E}{\partial T}\right)_v, \qquad 6:15$$

which represents the rate of change of E with temperature at constant volume. Also:

$$c_p = \left(\frac{\partial H}{\partial T}\right)_p, \qquad 6:16$$

which represents the rate of change of H with temperature at constant pressure.

Heat Capacity of Gases

If a monatomic gas (He or Hg) is heated at constant volume, the heat energy supplied is used only to increase the translational kinetic energy, KE, of the molecules. From Chapter 2, page 15:

$$KE = \tfrac{3}{2}pv,$$

and for one mole of a gas:

$$KE = \tfrac{3}{2}RT = \tfrac{3}{2}(1.99)T \cong 3T.$$

Let $3T_2$ represent the kinetic energy at T_2, and $3T_1$ the kinetic energy at T_1. The difference in kinetic energy is $3(T_2 - T_1)$. If $T_2 - T_1$ equals one, then the difference in kinetic energy is 3 cal./deg.-mole. The molar heat capacity at constant volume, C_v, is the number of calories required to raise the temperature of one mole one degree centigrade. Similarly, C_p is the molar heat capacity at constant pressure.

On the basis of the above argument, C_v for a monatomic gas should be 3 cal./deg.-mole and should be independent of the temperature. This has been confirmed experimentally and constitutes further proof for the validity of the postulates from which the fundamental kinetic equation is derived.

If the gas is heated at constant pressure, the gas expands and does work against the atmosphere. Then:

$$C_p - C_v = w = p\Delta v = p(v_2 - v_1) = R(T_2 - T_1).$$

If $T_2 - T_1 = 1$:

$$C_p - C_v = R \cong 2$$

and: $\qquad C_p = C_v + 2 = 3 + 2 = 5$ cal./deg.-mole.

Thus C_p for a monatomic gas should be 5 cal./deg.-mole. This has also been confirmed by experiment.

The ratio $\dfrac{C_p}{C_v}$ is given the symbol γ. For a monatomic gas:

$$\frac{C_p}{C_v} = \frac{5}{3} = 1.67.$$

For polyatomic molecules the situation is much more complicated and will not be discussed here.

Adiabatic Expansion of a Perfect Gas

An *adiabatic process* is one in which no heat enters or leaves the system. Then:
$$\Delta E = q - w = 0 - w = -w.$$

It is possible to derive the following equation which is applicable to the reversible, adiabatic expansion of a perfect gas:

$$C_v \ln \frac{T_2}{T_1} = -R \ln \frac{v_2}{v_1}.$$

By means of this equation the change in temperature in an adiabatic expansion or compression from v_1 to v_2 can be calculated.

Internal Energy of Gases

A system is represented by vessels A and B of equal volume separated by a stopcock. See Fig. 15. Vessel A contains a perfect gas

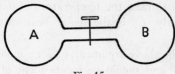

Fig. 15.

at a certain pressure. Vessel B is evacuated. The stopcock is opened and the gas rushes from A into B until the pressures in the two containers are equal. It is found that there is no evolution or absorption of heat between the system and the surroundings as a result of the expansion, or $q = 0$. Since the volume of the system $(A + B)$ remains constant, there is no external work done against the surroundings, or $w = 0$.

Then for the above change:

$$\Delta E = q - w = 0 - 0 = 0.$$

This result can be generalized into the following statement: $\Delta E = 0$ for any isothermal expansion or compression of a perfect gas, or mathematically stated:

$$\left(\frac{\partial E}{\partial v}\right)_T = 0.$$

This is one of the two criteria of a perfect gas. The other is that the gas must obey the perfect-gas law.

Thermochemistry

Thermochemistry deals with the heat changes which accompany chemical reactions. The heat evolved (or absorbed) depends on: (1) the amounts of substances involved; (2) the physical states of the substances involved; (3) the temperature; (4) whether the reaction occurs at constant pressure or constant volume; and (5) the pressure. Pressure has little effect on the heat of reaction and will not be considered further. If the heat of reaction at either constant pressure or constant volume is known, the other can be calculated from equation 6:12.

Thermochemical Equations. A thermochemical equation is used to summarize the heat change in a chemical reaction. For example, at 25° C.:

In order to evaluate the absolute entropy a plot is made of C_p versus log T. A typical C_p versus log T graph for a solid is shown in Fig. 16.

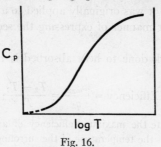

Fig. 16.

The area under the curve from $T = 0$ to $T = T$ is determined and multiplied by 2.303. This gives the absolute entropy of the substance at the temperature T. Experimental measurements of C_p can be made as low as 10 to 15 degrees K. Below this temperature the extrapolation to $0°$ K. can be made with various semiempirical equations. If a transition, such as fusion, vaporization, or sublimation, occurs, there will be a discontinuity in the C_p versus log T curve, and a $\Delta S = \dfrac{q_{rev.}}{T}$ term for each change will have to be added to ΔS as calculated from the graphical integration.

Physical Significance of Entropy

Entropy can be considered as a measure of the disorder of a system. A pure crystalline substance at $0°$ K. consists of stationary ions, atoms, or molecules perfectly arranged in the crystal lattice; the entropy is zero. At a temperature greater than $0°$ K. the units of the crystal lattice vibrate about a fixed position, thus giving rise to an increase in S. Upon further heating, the solid finally melts, most of the order is destroyed, and the entropy increases further. Vaporization results in another increase of disorder and also of S.

Conversion of Heat into Work in a Reversible Cycle

The maximum work which can be done by an engine in a reversible cycle is:

$$w_{max.} = q_2 \cdots \qquad \text{6:23}$$

in which: q_2 = heat absorbed by engine from a reservoir at temperature the surroundings.

T_1 = temper

This equation can be derived by considering the sequence of operations called the Carnot cycle. Equation 6:23 is applicable to any substance although it was originally applied to a perfect gas. Equation 6:23 is another manner of expressing the second law of thermodynamics.

The ratio of work done to heat absorbed is the efficiency of the process. Hence:

$$\text{Efficiency} = \frac{w_{max.}}{q_2} = \frac{T_2 - T_1}{T_2}. \qquad 6:24$$

Example. Calculate the maximum efficiency of an engine if it absorbs heat at 100° C. and if the temperature of the surroundings is 25° C.

$$\text{Efficiency} = \frac{w_{max.}}{q_2} = \frac{T_2 - T_1}{T_2}$$

$$= \frac{373 - 298}{373} = 0.201 = 20.1\%.$$

Free Energy and Work Content

Free energy, F, is defined as:

$$F = H - TS \qquad 6:25$$

and represents that portion of the heat content which is isothermally available. Work content, A, is defined as:

$$A = E - TS \qquad 6:26$$

and represents that part of the internal energy which is isothermally available. Like internal energy, F and A depend only on the initial and final states of the system.

From the above:

$$\Delta F = \Delta H - \Delta(TS) \qquad 6:27$$

or at constant temperature:

$$\Delta F = \Delta H - T\Delta S, \qquad 6:28$$

and:

$$\Delta A = \Delta E - \Delta(TS) \qquad 6:29$$

or at constant temperature:

$$\Delta A = \Delta E - T\Delta S. \qquad 6:30$$

Since $H = E + pv$ (equation 6:8) and $H = F + TS$, then:

$$F = E + pv \qquad 6:31$$

and:

$$F = E - TS + pv \qquad 6:32$$

or, since $A = E - TS$:

$$F = A + pv. \qquad 6:33$$

Then: $$\Delta F = \Delta A + \Delta(pv) \qquad \textbf{6:34}$$
or at constant pressure:
$$\Delta F = \Delta A + p\Delta v. \qquad \textbf{6:35}$$

For a change at constant temperature, ΔA has a simple physical meaning; since:

$$\Delta S = \frac{q_{\text{rev.}}}{T},$$
$$q_{\text{rev.}} = T\Delta S,$$
$$\Delta A = \Delta E - T\Delta S,$$

then $\Delta A = \Delta E - q_{\text{rev.}}$, and for a reversible process:

$$\Delta E = q_{\text{rev.}} - w_{\text{max.}},$$
$$\Delta E - q_{\text{rev.}} = -w_{\text{max.}}.$$

Hence: $$\Delta A = -w_{\text{max.}}. \qquad \textbf{6:36}$$

Thermodynamic Calculations

A grasp of the significance of q, w, ΔE, ΔH, ΔF, ΔA, and ΔS is best achieved through the solution of various problems which illustrate the quantitative interrelationships involved. Applications to some physical changes are illustrated here. Applications to chemical reactions will be found in subsequent chapters.

Example. One mole of water is vaporized reversibly at 100° C. and 1 atm. Calculate q, w, ΔE, ΔH, ΔA, ΔF, and ΔS.

$$H_2O_{(l)} \rightleftarrows H_2O_{(g)}.$$

In a previous example (p. 43) it was shown that:

$$q = 9720 \text{ cal.}$$
$$w = p\Delta v = 742 \text{ cal.}$$
$$\Delta E = 8978 \text{ cal.}$$

Since the process is at constant pressure:

$$\Delta H = q_p = 9720 \text{ cal.}$$

Since the process is reversible:

$$\Delta A = -w_{\text{max.}} = -742 \text{ cal.}$$
$$\Delta F = \Delta A + p\Delta v = (-742) + (742) = 0.$$
$$\Delta S = \frac{q_{\text{rev.}}}{T} = \frac{9720}{373} = 26.1 \text{ cal./deg.-mole.}$$

Example. One mole of a perfect gas expands isothermally and reversibly from 1 liter to 10 liters at 300° K. Calculate ΔE, q, w, ΔH, ΔA, ΔF, and ΔS.

$$\Delta E = 0. \quad \text{(See p. 48.)}$$

$$q_{rev.} = w_{max.} = 2.30 \, nRT \, \log \frac{v_2}{v_1}$$

$$= (2.30)(1)(1.99)(300) \log \frac{10}{1}$$

$$= 1370 \text{ cal.}$$

$$\Delta(pv) = p_2 v_2 - p_1 v_1 = 0 \text{ for a perfect gas;}$$
$$\Delta H = \Delta E + \Delta(pv) = 0 + 0 = 0.$$
$$\Delta A = - w_{max.} = -1370 \text{ cal.}$$
$$\Delta F = \Delta A + \Delta(pv)$$
$$= (-1370) + (0) = -1370 \text{ cal.}$$
$$\Delta S = \frac{q_{rev.}}{T} = \frac{1370}{300} = 4.57 \text{ cal./deg.-mole.}$$

Criteria for Spontaneous Processes

It can be shown that for a process in which the initial and final temperatures and pressures are the same:

1. if ΔF is positive, the process is not spontaneous;
2. if ΔF is negative, the process is spontaneous;
3. If ΔF is zero, the system is in equilibrium.

Only a brief outline of the proof of the above can be given here. For a system at constant pressure and temperature, $F = E + pv - TS$, and therefore:

$$\Delta F = \Delta E + p\Delta v - T\Delta S.$$

But for a reversible process at constant temperature:

$$q_{rev.} = T\Delta S \quad \text{and} \quad \Delta E = q_{rev.} - w_{max.}.$$

Combining:

$$\Delta F = -w_{max.} + p\Delta v.$$

However, for a reversible process at constant pressure:

$$w_{max.} = p\Delta v.$$

Hence:
$$\Delta F = -w_{max.} + p\Delta v = 0.$$

Thus at constant temperature and pressure if ΔF equals zero, the process must be reversible, which means that the system is in a state of equilibrium.

For a reversible process:

$$dS = \frac{dq_{rev.}}{T}.$$

However, any naturally occurring or spontaneous process can never be completely reversible because of such effects as frictional losses.

For such spontaneous processes, the entropy change is greater than the heat absorbed from the surroundings divided by T, or:

$$dS > \frac{dq}{T}$$

or:
$$\Delta S > \frac{q}{T}$$

for a spontaneous process, or:

$$T\Delta S > q.$$

Since at constant temperature:

$$\Delta F = \Delta H - T\Delta S$$

and at constant pressure:

$$\Delta H = q_p,$$

then at both constant temperature and pressure:

$$\Delta F = q_p - T\Delta S.$$

Now if $T\Delta S$ is greater than q_p, then ΔF is negative. However, $T\Delta S$ is greater than q_p only for a spontaneous process; hence if ΔF is positive, the process must then be nonspontaneous. The above criterion for spontaneity can be applied to chemical reactions as well as to physical changes.

The Clapeyron Equation

The equation which expresses the rate of change of the vapor pressure of a liquid with temperature, originally derived by Clapeyron (1834), is:

$$\frac{dp}{dT} = \frac{l}{T(v_2 - v_1)}, \qquad \textbf{6:37}$$

in which: $v_2 =$ volume of 1 gram of the substance in the vapor state,
$v_1 =$ volume of 1 gram of the substance in the liquid state,
$l =$ heat of vaporization per gram,
$\dfrac{dp}{dT} =$ rate of change of vapor pressure of a liquid with temperature,
$T =$ temperature.

However, this equation is also applicable to transition from one crystal form to another, to fusion, and to sublimation. Then:

$v_2 =$ volume of 1 gram of substance in the final state,
$v_1 =$ volume of 1 gram of substance in the initial state,
$l =$ heat of change of state or heat of transition per gram,
$T =$ temperature.

Note. It is necessary that l have the same units as the product of pressure and volume change. If pressure is in atmospheres and volume change is in milliliters, l must be in ml.-atm. Since tables usually give l in calories, it is necessary to convert units by use of the following equation: 1 calorie = 41.3 ml.-atm.

Example. Calculate the change in volume accompanying the fusion of one gram of phenol at its melting point, given:

$$t = 41° \text{ C.}; \quad T = 273 + 41 = 314° \text{ K.}$$
$$l = \text{heat of fusion in cal./gram} = 24.9.$$
$$\frac{dp}{dT} = 231 \text{ atm./deg.}$$

This means that an increase of pressure of 231 atm. will raise the melting point of phenol 1° C. Then:

$$\frac{dp}{dT} = \frac{l}{T(v_2 - v_1)}.$$
$$231 = \frac{(24.9)(41.3)}{(314)(\Delta v)}.$$
$$\Delta v = 0.0142 \text{ ml.}$$

The Clausius-Clapeyron Equation

Clausius showed that the Clapeyron equation can be simplified by application of the perfect-gas law. If one mole is considered instead of one gram, then:

$$L_v = \text{molar heat of vaporization,}$$
$$V_2 = \text{volume of one mole of the vapor,}$$
$$V_1 = \text{volume of one mole of the liquid.}$$

Then:
$$\frac{dp}{dT} = \frac{L_v}{T(V_2 - V_1)}.$$
6:38

However, V_1 is negligible compared to V_2. Then:

$$\frac{dp}{dT} = \frac{L_v}{T(V_2)}.$$
6:39

Since V_2 represents the volume of one mole of a gas, it can be replaced by $\frac{RT}{p}$. Then:

$$\frac{dp}{dT} = \frac{L_v}{T\left(\dfrac{RT}{p}\right)} = \frac{pL_v}{RT^2}.$$
6:40

Rearranging:
$$\frac{dp}{p} = \frac{L_v}{R}\frac{dT}{T^2}.$$
6:41

$$d \ln p = \frac{L_v}{R} \frac{dT}{T^2}. \qquad \textbf{6:42}$$

Assuming that L_v is a constant:

$$\int d \ln p = \frac{L_v}{R} \int \frac{dT}{T^2}. \qquad \textbf{6:43}$$

$$\ln p + C' = -\frac{L_v}{R} \frac{1}{T} + C''. \qquad \textbf{6:44}$$

$$\ln p = -\frac{L_v}{R} \frac{1}{T} + C, \qquad \textbf{6:45}$$

in which: $\qquad C = C'' - C'.$

$$\log p = \frac{-L_v}{2.303R} \frac{1}{T} + \frac{C}{2.303}. \qquad \textbf{6:46}$$

Thus, if $\log p$ is plotted versus $\frac{1}{T}$, a straight line is obtained whose slope is $\frac{-L_v}{2.303R}.$ The theoretical justification for the straight-line relationship in Fig. 7 of Chapter 3 is now apparent.

A more convenient form of the Clausius-Clapeyron equation is obtained by integrating between limits.

$$\int_{p_1}^{p_2} d \ln p = \frac{L_v}{R} \int_{T_1}^{T_2} \frac{dT}{T^2}. \qquad \textbf{6:47}$$

$$\ln \frac{p_2}{p_1} = \frac{L_v}{R}\left[\left(-\frac{1}{T_2}\right) - \left(-\frac{1}{T_1}\right)\right]. \qquad \textbf{6:48}$$

$$\ln \frac{p_2}{p_1} = \frac{L_v(T_2 - T_1)}{RT_1T_2}. \qquad \textbf{6:49}$$

$$\log \frac{p_2}{p_1} = \frac{L_v(T_2 - T_1)}{2.303RT_1T_2}. \qquad \textbf{6:50}$$

Since it has been assumed that L_v is constant in equation 6:47, the temperature range must not be too great. Any pressure units may be used; L_v and R must have the same units. Equation 6:50 can be used for sublimation if L_s (the molar heat of sublimation) is substituted for L_v, but equation 6:50 cannot be used for transition from one crystal form to another or for fusion.

Example. The vapor pressure of water at 100° C. is 760 mm. Calculate the vapor pressure at 90° C.; L_v is 9720 cal./mole.

$$\log \frac{760}{p_1} = \frac{(9720)(373 - 363)}{(2.30)(1.99)(363)(373)}.$$

$$\log p_1 = \log 760 - \frac{(9720)(373 - 363)}{(2.30)(1.99)(363)(373)}$$

$$= 2.8808 - 0.1570$$

$$= 2.7238.$$

$$p_1 = 529 \text{ mm.}$$

Review Questions and Problems

1. State the first law of thermodynamics in words and in the form of an equation.

2. Derive: (a) $w = p\Delta v$; (b) $w_{max.} = nRT \ln \frac{v_2}{v_1}$.

3. Define a reversible process and give two examples.

4. Prove that $\Delta E = q_v$ and $\Delta H = q_p$.

5. Show that C_p for a perfect monatomic gas would be expected to be 5 cal./deg.-mole and to be independent of temperature.

6. Upon what factors does the heat evolved in a chemical reaction depend?

7. State Hess's law of constant heat summation.

8. Define heat of formation.

9. State the second law of thermodynamics in two different ways.

10. Define entropy.

11. State the third law of thermodynamics.

12. Prove that $\Delta A = -w_{max.}$ for a change at constant temperature.

13. Derive equation 6:50 starting with the Clapeyron equation.

14. One mole of benzene is condensed reversibly at its boiling point (80.1° C.) and 1 atm. Calculate q, w, ΔE, ΔH, ΔF, ΔA, and ΔS. The heat of vaporization is 7350 cal./mole.

15. One mole of a perfect gas is compressed at 100° C. reversibly and isothermally from a volume of 2 liters to a volume of 1 liter. Calculate q, w, ΔE, ΔH, ΔF, ΔA, and ΔS.

16. Calculate ΔE for the following reaction at 25° C.:

$$C_2H_{4(g)} + 3 O_{2(g)} \rightarrow 2 CO_{2(g)} + 2 H_2O_{(l)}.$$

$\Delta H = -337$ kcal.

17. Two moles of a perfect gas is cooled from 298° K. to 273° K. at constant pressure. Calculate ΔS. $C_p = 5$ cal./deg.-mole.

18. Calculate the maximum efficiency of an engine which uses Hg vapor at 400° C. as the source of heat in surroundings at 25° C.

19. Calculate the heat of fusion of acetic acid at its melting point (16.6° C.).

$$\frac{dp}{dT} = 41.3 \text{ atm./deg.;} \quad v_2 - v_1 = 0.160 \text{ ml.}$$

20. The boiling point (at 1 atm.) of a certain hydrocarbon is 100° C. $L_v = 7800$ cal./mole. Calculate vapor pressure at 95° C.

21. Calculate ΔH for the following reaction at 25° C.

$$CH_{4(g)} + 2\ O_{2(g)} \to CO_{2(g)} + 2\ H_2O_{(l)}$$

using the data in Table 5.

7

Solutions

A solution is a homogeneous mixture of two or more substances, the relative proportions of which may vary between certain limits. This chapter is concerned with the principal laws governing the behavior of solutions of liquids in liquids and solids in liquids.

Vapor-Pressure Relationships

The effect of concentration upon the vapor pressure of a solution will be dealt with first.

Raoult's Law. According to Raoult's law for a solution of A in B:

$$p_A = \frac{n_A}{n_A + n_B}\, p^0{}_A = N_A p^0{}_A \qquad\qquad 7{:}1$$

and:

$$p_B = \frac{n_B}{n_A + n_B}\, p^0{}_B = N_B p^0{}_B, \qquad\qquad 7{:}2$$

in which:
p_A = partial pressure of component A in the solution,
$p^0{}_A$ = vapor pressure of pure A,
p_B = partial pressure of component B in the solution,
$p^0{}_B$ = vapor pressure of pure B,
n_A = moles of A in the solution,
n_B = moles of B in the solution,
N_A = mole fraction of A,
N_B = mole fraction of B.

It is convenient to speak of ideal or perfect solutions, just as in the chapter on gases it was convenient to speak of ideal or perfect gases. Two important criteria of ideal solutions are: (1) that they obey Raoult's law, and (2) that no heat is absorbed or evolved when more solvent is added.

The vapor-pressure relationships of ideal solutions of A and B at a given temperature are shown in Fig. 17.

In an ideal solution the behavior of each substance is unaffected by the presence of the other. Therefore, the vapor pressure of the solution is the sum of the vapor pressure of A plus the vapor pressure of B. Ideal solutions are likely to be obtained if A and B are similar chemically. An example is a solution of benzene and toluene.

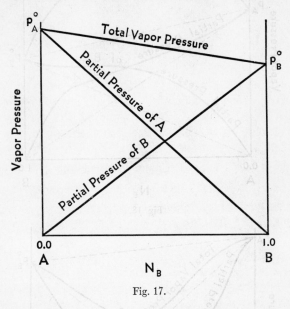

Fig. 17.

Positive Deviations from Raoult's Law. Both positive and negative deviations from Raoult's law are known. If the attraction of A for A is decreased by the presence of B and the attraction of B for B is decreased by the presence of A, then the vapor pressure of the solution is greater than would be expected from Raoult's law. If this positive deviation is sufficiently pronounced, the vapor pressure curve of the solution may exhibit a maximum which is above the vapor pressure of either pure component. See Fig. 18 (p. 64).

The dotted lines in Fig. 18 represent ideal behavior. An example of such a system is a solution of acetone and carbon disulfide.

Negative Deviations from Raoult's Law. If the attractive forces between A and B are greater than the attractive forces between A and A and between B and B, the observed vapor pressure is less than that calculated from Raoult's law. If this negative deviation is sufficiently pronounced, the vapor pressure curve of the solution exhibits a minimum which is less than the vapor pressure of either pure component. An example is a solution of acetone and chloroform. See Fig. 19.

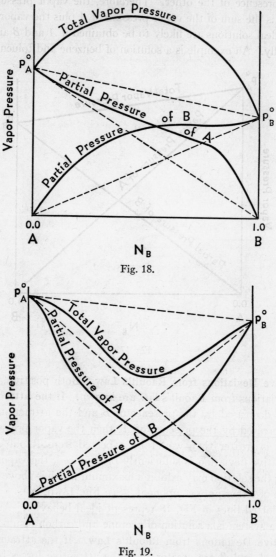

Fig. 18.

Fig. 19.

Distillation Phenomena and Boiling-Point Diagrams

When homogeneous, binary, liquid solutions are distilled at constant pressure, they fall into the following types:

1. Solutions whose boiling points are all intermediate between the boiling points of the pure components.

2. Solutions whose boiling points show a maximum which is greater than the boiling point of either pure component. Such solutions also show minima in the vapor-pressure curve of Fig. 19.

3. Solutions whose boiling points show a minimum which is less than the boiling point of either pure component. Such solutions also show maxima in the vapor-pressure curve of Fig. 18.

Type 1 Diagrams. The boiling-point diagram for a solution of type 1 is shown in Fig. 20.

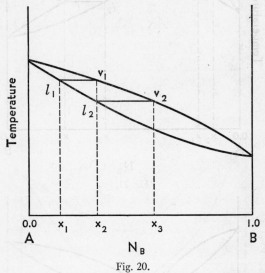

Fig. 20.

The lower curve represents the boiling temperatures of all mixtures of A and B at the given pressure. The upper curve represents the composition of the vapor in equilibrium with the solution. To determine the composition of the vapor in equilibrium with a solution of a given mole fraction of B, a horizontal line is drawn from the appropriate point of the boiling-point curve to the vapor-composition curve.

For example, if a solution of composition x_1 is heated, it will start to boil at a temperature corresponding to l_1, and the first vapor, v_1, which comes off at this temperature has the composition x_2. As distillation proceeds the liquid remaining becomes poorer in the more volatile component B, and the boiling point rises until only pure A is left in the distilling flask. If the vapor v_1 is cooled until it liquefies and then boiled, the vapor v_2 which comes off has the composition x_3, which is richer in B than the vapor v_1. Thus by continued condensation and distillation it is possible to obtain pure B in the distillate and pure A in the residue.

Types 2 and 3 Diagrams. The boiling-point diagrams for solutions of types 2 and 3 are shown in Figs. 21 and 22 respectively. In Fig. 21,

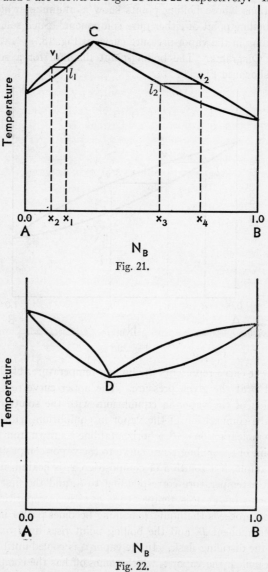

Fig. 21.

Fig. 22.

if liquid of composition x_1 is distilled, the vapor v_1 coming off initially
has the composition x_2. On continued distillation the boiling point
rises until liquid of composition C remains in the distilling flask. Then
liquid and vapor have the same composition, and distillation proceeds until all the liquid has boiled away. A solution which distills
without change in composition or temperature is called an *azeotrope*.
The vapor v_1 could be separated into pure A and a mixture of composition C by repeated condensation and distillation.

If liquid of composition x_3 is distilled, the vapor v_2 which comes off
initially has the composition x_4. On continued distillation the boiling
point rises until the azeotrope represented by composition C is obtained. The vapor v_2 can be separated into pure B and the azeotrope
C by repeated condensation and distillation.

Thus any mixture of type 2 having a composition between pure A
and C can be separated by fractional distillation only into a distillate
of pure A and a final residue of C. No pure B is obtainable by fractional distillation. If the composition lies between C and pure B,
only a distillate of B and a final residue of C can be obtained.

The behavior of type 3 solutions (Fig. 22) is similar except that the
residue tends toward pure components and the distillates tend toward
the minimum boiling azeotrope, D.

Steam Distillation

If two liquids are immiscible, each will exert its own vapor pressure
independently of the other. This phenomenon is applied in the steam
distillation of high-boiling organic liquids. Distillation occurs at that
temperature at which the sum of the vapor pressures of the two liquids
just exceeds the atmospheric pressure. The pressure of a vapor is
proportional to the moles of vapor per unit volume. Hence for two
liquids A and B:

$$\frac{p_A}{p_B} = \frac{n_A}{n_B} = \frac{\dfrac{g_A}{M_A}}{\dfrac{g_B}{M_B}}, \qquad\qquad 7:3$$

in which: p_A = vapor pressure of A at the given temperature,

p_B = vapor pressure of B at the given temperature,

n_A = moles of A in the vapor,

n_B = moles of B in the vapor,

M_A = molecular weight of A,

M_B = molecular weight of B,

g_A = grams of A,

g_B = grams of B.

Example. A mixture of water and bromobenzene was steam-distilled at 95° C. The distillate contained 58.0 grams of water and 100 grams of bromobenzene. Calculate the molecular weight of bromobenzene if the vapor pressures of water and bromobenzene at the given temperature are 635 and 125 mm., respectively.

$$\frac{635}{125} = \frac{\dfrac{58}{18}}{\dfrac{100}{M}}.$$

$$M = 158.$$

Dilute Solutions of Nonvolatile Nonelectrolytes

If a nonvolatile nonelectrolyte is dissolved in a liquid the vapor pressure is lowered, the boiling point is elevated, the freezing point is depressed, and the phenomenon known as osmotic pressure manifests itself. These four colligative properties are all interrelated and may be used to calculate molecular weights and other significant properties.

Vapor-Pressure Lowering. According to a form of Raoult's law applicable to a dilute solution containing a nonvolatile nonelectrolyte:

$$\frac{p^0 - p}{p^0} = \frac{n_2}{n_1 + n_2} = N_2, \qquad \textbf{7:4}$$

in which subscripts 1 and 2 indicate solvent and solute respectively and:

$p^0 =$ vapor pressure of pure solvent,
$p =$ vapor pressure of the solution,
$n_2 =$ moles of solute,
$n_1 =$ moles of solvent,
$N_2 =$ mole fraction of solute.

In dilute solutions, n_2 may be neglected in comparison to n_1.

The vapor pressure is lowered because some of the volatile solvent molecules in the surface layer are replaced by nonvolatile solute molecules. The lowering depends simply on the number of solute molecules present and not on their kind. Hence, vapor-pressure lowering is a colligative property.

Example. Ten grams of a certain nonvolatile nonelectrolyte was dissolved in 100 grams of water at 20° C. The vapor pressure was lowered from 17.535 to 17.235 mm. Calculate the molecular weight of the solute.

$$\frac{17.535 - 17.235}{17.535} = \frac{\dfrac{10}{M}}{\dfrac{100}{18}}.$$

$$M = 105.$$

Boiling-Point Elevation. Since the vapor pressure is lowered by the addition of a nonvolatile nonelectrolyte, it follows that the boiling point of a solution must be raised. This is evident from Fig. 23.

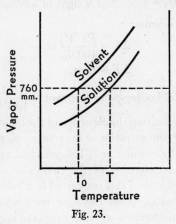

Fig. 23.

It is seen that the vapor pressure of the solution reaches 760 mm. at a higher temperature than the vapor pressure of the solvent. Hence, the boiling point, T, of the solution is higher than the boiling point, T_0, of the solvent. From the Clausius-Clapeyron equation:

$$\frac{dp}{dT} = \frac{pL_v}{RT^2}$$

or for small changes:

$$\frac{\Delta p}{\Delta T} = \frac{pL_v}{RT^2};$$

$$\Delta T = \frac{RT^2}{L_v} \frac{\Delta p}{p}.$$

Since Raoult's Law is:

$$\frac{\Delta p}{p} = \frac{n_2}{n_1 + n_2},$$

then the elevation of the boiling point, ΔT, is:

$$\Delta T = \frac{RT^2}{L_v} \frac{n_2}{n_1 + n_2},$$

or for dilute solutions:

$$\Delta T = \frac{RT^2}{L_v} \frac{n_2}{n_1}.$$ 7:5

It follows from the definition of molality that:

$$\frac{n_2}{n_1} = \frac{m}{1000/M_1},$$

in which: m = molality of solution,

M_1 = molecular weight of solvent,

and equation 7:5 becomes:

$$\Delta T = \frac{RT^2M_1}{1000L_v} m$$ 7:6

or: $$\Delta T = K_b m,$$ 7:7

in which K_b = molal boiling-point constant = $\dfrac{RT^2M_1}{1000L_v}$.

Thus for a dilute solution the elevation of the boiling point is directly proportional to the concentration of the solute. K_b may be determined experimentally or by calculation. The principal application of equation 7:6 is the determination of the molecular weights of solutes. For this purpose equation 7:6 is converted to a more convenient form.

Let ΔT be the boiling-point elevation for a solution containing g_2 grams of solute of molecular weight M_2 dissolved in g_1 grams of solvent. Then the weight of solute per 1000 grams of solvent is:

$$\frac{1000g_2}{g_1},$$

and the molality is:

$$m = \frac{1000g_2}{g_1M_2},$$

and equation 7:7 becomes:

$$\Delta T = K_b \frac{1000g_2}{g_1M_2}.$$ 7:8

K_b for several solvents is given in Table 6.

TABLE 6

MOLAL BOILING-POINT CONSTANTS

Solvent	Boiling Point in ° C.	K_b
Benzene	80.2	2.57
Chloroform	60.2	3.63
Water	100.0	0.51
Acetone	56.0	1.71

Example. If 10 grams of a certain nonvolatile nonelectrolyte is dissolved in 100 grams of benzene, $\Delta T = 3.10°$ C. Calculate the molecular weight of the solute.

$$M_2 = K_b \frac{1000 \ g_2}{g_1 \Delta T} = \frac{(2.57)(1000)(10)}{(100)(3.10)} = 82.9.$$

Freezing-Point Depression. As a consequence of the lowering of the vapor pressure by the addition of a nonvolatile nonelectrolyte, the freezing point is depressed. It is possible to derive the following equation in a manner similar to that used in deriving equation 7:8:

$$\Delta T = K_f \frac{1000 g_2}{g_1 M_2}, \qquad \textbf{7:9}$$

in which: ΔT = observed lowering of freezing point,

K_f = molal freezing-point constant.

Values of K_f for several solvents are given in Table 7. Equation 7:9 may be used to calculate molecular weights in a manner similar to that used in the example above.

TABLE 7

MOLAL FREEZING-POINT CONSTANTS

Solvent	Freezing Point in ° C.	K_f
Benzene	5.4	5.12
Acetic Acid	17.0	3.90
Camphor	178.4	37.70
Water	0.0	1.86

Osmotic Pressure. *Osmosis* is the passage of a solvent through a membrane from a dilute solution to a more concentrated one. The essential property of a membrane in osmosis is that it be permeable to the solvent but not to the solute. Such a membrane is said to be *semipermeable.*

Osmotic pressure may be defined as the excess pressure which must be applied to a solution to prevent the passage of solvent into it when separated from the solvent by a semipermeable membrane. The osmotic pressure of a dilute solution can be calculated by means of an equation analogous to the perfect-gas law:

$$\pi v = nRT \qquad \textbf{7:10}$$

in which: π = osmotic pressure of the solution,

v = volume of solvent.

Example. 10 grams of urea (molecular weight = 60.1) is dissolved in 1.0 liter of water. Calculate the osmotic pressure of the solution at 20° C.

$$\pi = \frac{n}{v} RT$$

$$= \frac{\left(\frac{10}{60.1}\right)(0.0820)(293)}{1.0}$$

$$= 4.00 \text{ atm.}$$

Many theories have been proposed to explain the mechanism of osmosis. The three most important are:

1. *The Vapor-Pressure Theory.* It is assumed that the membrane is made up of fine capillaries which are too small to allow the passage of liquid solvent but through which distillation can take place from the more dilute to the more concentrated solution.

2. *The Molecular-Sieve Theory.* It is assumed that the solvent molecules are small enough to pass through the openings in the membrane whereas the solute particles are too large to pass through. This theory is applicable only to extremely large solute molecules or to particles of colloidal size.

3. *The Membrane-Solution Theory.* It is assumed that the solvent dissolves in (and hence passes through) the membrane whereas the solute does not.

It is well to emphasize at this point that equations 7:4, 7:8, 7:9, and 7:10 apply only to *dilute* solutions of *nonvolatile nonelectrolytes.*

Solutions of Electrolytes

The freezing-point depressions, boiling-point elevations, vapor-pressure lowerings, and osmotic pressures of solutions of electrolytes are all abnormally high. This is due to the presence of ions. Since the four properties named above are colligative, they depend only on the number of particles present, be they molecules, atoms, or ions. One mole of sucrose dissolved in 1000 grams of water yields 6.02×10^{23} molecules. However, one mole of NaCl when dissolved in 1000 grams of water yields 12.04×10^{23} ions. Hence a one-molal solution of NaCl should freeze at $2(-1.86)$ or $-3.72°$ C. The actual value is $-3.42°$ C. The discrepancy can be explained in terms of the interionic-attraction theory discussed in Chapter 13, p. 145. The van't Hoff factor, i, is defined as:

$$i = \frac{\Delta p}{(\Delta p)_0} = \frac{\Delta T_b}{(\Delta T_b)_0} = \frac{\Delta T_f}{(\Delta T_f)_0} = \frac{\pi}{\pi_0}, \qquad \textbf{7:11}$$

in which: Δp = observed vapor-pressure lowering for a solution of an electrolyte,

$(\Delta p)_0$ = normal vapor-pressure lowering as calculated from equation 7:4,

ΔT_b = observed boiling-point rise for a solution of an electrolyte,

$(\Delta T_b)_0$ = normal boiling-point rise as calculated from equation 7:8,

ΔT_f = observed freezing-point depression for a solution of an electrolyte,

$(\Delta T_f)_0$ = normal freezing-point depression as calculated from equation 7:9,

π = observed osmotic pressure for a solution of an electrolyte,

π_0 = normal osmotic pressure as calculated from equation 7:10.

As the solution becomes more dilute, $i \rightarrow$ the number of ions formed from one molecule [e.g., two for KCl, three for $BaCl_2$, and four for $K_3Fe(CN)_6$].

The van't Hoff factor is useful in calculating colligative properties of solutions of electrolytes.

Example.   A 0.100-molal solution of NH_4Cl freezes at $-0.344°$ C. Calculate i and ΔT_b.

$$\Delta T_f = 0.344.$$

$$(\Delta T_f)_0 = K_f \frac{1000 g_2}{g_1 M_2} = 1.86 \frac{(1000)(5.35)}{(1000)(53.5)}$$

$$= 0.186.$$

$$i = \frac{0.344}{0.186} = 1.85.$$

$$\Delta T_b = i(\Delta T_b)_0 = i K_b \frac{1000 g_2}{g_1 M_2}$$

$$= (1.85)(0.51) \frac{(1000)(5.35)}{(1000)(53.5)}$$

$$= 0.0944° \text{ C.}$$

Review Questions and Problems

1. State Raoult's law in terms of two equations.   Define each symbol used.

2. Draw and discuss the boiling-point diagrams for solutions of types 1, 2, and 3.

3. Derive:
$$\Delta T = K_b \frac{1000 g_2}{g_1 M_2}.$$

4. How many grams of bromobenzene can be steam-distilled by 1000 grams of water at 95° C.?

5. Thirty grams of a certain nonvolatile nonelectrolyte is dissolved in 1000 grams of water at 20° C. If the molecular weight of the solute is 100, calculate the vapor pressure of the solution. Vapor pressure of water at 20° C. is 17.5 mm.

6. Twenty-five grams of sucrose (molecular weight = 342) is dissolved in 1000 grams of water. Calculate the boiling point, freezing point, and osmotic pressure (at 25° C.) of the solution.

7. The freezing point of a 0.100-molal K_2SO_4 solution is $-0.432°$ C. Calculate the osmotic pressure of the solution at 25° C.

8

Chemical Equilibria and Free Energy

Chemical equilibrium occurs when opposing reactions take place at the same rate.

The Law of Mass Action and Equilibrium Constants

According to the law of mass action the rate of a chemical reaction is directly proportional to the molar concentrations of the reacting substances. Consider the reaction:

$$A + B \rightleftarrows G + H, \qquad\qquad 8{:}1$$

in which: A and B represent the reactants,
               G and H represent the products.

If some A and B are mixed, the rate of the forward reaction is fast and the rate of the reverse reaction is zero since no G and H are present. After some G and H are formed the reverse reaction speeds up and the forward reaction slows down (since there are less A and B left). The rate of the forward reaction continues to decrease and the rate of the reverse reaction continues to increase until the two rates become equal and just offset each other. Then no further change in composition with time takes place, and the system is said to have reached a state of chemical equilibrium.

Equilibrium Constant K_c. It follows from the law of mass action that:

$$\text{rate of forward reaction} \propto c_A c_B = k_1 c_A c_B,$$
$$\text{rate of reverse reaction} \propto c_G c_H = k_2 c_G c_H,$$

in which: c = molar concentration of substance indicated by subscript,
          k_1 = proportionality constant for the forward reaction,
          k_2 = proportionality constant for the reverse reaction.

At equilibrium the rate of the forward reaction is equal to the rate of the reverse reaction, or:

$$k_1 c_A c_B = k_2 c_G c_H.$$

$$K_c = \frac{k_1}{k_2} = \frac{c_G c_H}{c_A c_B}, \qquad \qquad \textbf{8:2}$$

in which K_c = equilibrium constant expressed in terms of concentrations.

Equation 8:2 expresses the quantitative relationship between the concentrations of reactants and products present at equilibrium for a reaction of the type shown in equation 8:1.

Example. If 1 mole of ethyl alcohol and 1 mole of acetic acid are mixed at 25° C. and allowed to come to equilibrium, $\frac{2}{3}$ mole of ethyl acetate and $\frac{2}{3}$ mole of water are formed. Calculate K_c.

$$C_2H_5OH + CH_3COOH \rightleftharpoons CH_3COOC_2H_5 + H_2O.$$

Let v = volume of solution. At equilibrium:

$$c_{\text{alcohol}} = c_{\text{acid}} = \frac{1 - \frac{2}{3}}{v} = \frac{\frac{1}{3}}{v} \text{ mole/liter.}$$

$$c_{\text{ester}} = c_{H_2O} = \frac{\frac{2}{3}}{v} \text{ mole/liter.}$$

$$K_c = \frac{c_{\text{ester}} \, c_{H_2O}}{c_{\text{alcohol}} \, c_{\text{acid}}} = \frac{\left(\frac{\frac{2}{3}}{v}\right)\left(\frac{\frac{2}{3}}{v}\right)}{\left(\frac{\frac{1}{3}}{v}\right)\left(\frac{\frac{1}{3}}{v}\right)} = 4.00.$$

Example. How many moles of ester are formed at equilibrium if 3 moles of acetic acid are mixed with 1 mole of alcohol?

Let x = moles of ester formed at equilibrium. Then:

$$K = 4.00 = \frac{(x)(x)}{(1 - x)(3 - x)}.$$

$$x = 0.9 \text{ or } 4.4.$$

0.9 mole of ester is formed.

Note. The root 4.4 of the quadratic is obviously impossible in the problem.

General Equation for K_c. The process considered in equation 8:1 involves only one molecule of each of the reactants and each of the products. The situation is more complicated if more than one molecule of a reactant or product is involved. The reaction:

$$N_2 + 3\,H_2 \rightleftharpoons 2\,NH_3 \qquad \qquad \textbf{8:3}$$

can be rewritten:

$$N_2 + H_2 + H_2 + H_2 \rightleftharpoons NH_3 + NH_3.$$

Then at equilibrium when the rate of forward reaction equals the rate of reverse reaction:

$$k_1 c_{N_2} c_{H_2} c_{H_2} c_{H_2} = k_2 c_{NH_3} c_{NH_3}.$$
$$k_1 c_{N_2} c_{H_2}^3 = k_2 c_{NH_3}^2.$$

$$K_c = \frac{k_1}{k_2} = \frac{c_{NH_3}^2}{c_{N_2} c_{H_2}^3}. \qquad\qquad 8:4$$

Note that the coefficients used in balancing equation 8:3 appear as exponents in the equilibrium-constant expression. In the general equation:

$$aA + bB + \cdots \rightleftarrows gG + hH + \cdots, \qquad\qquad 8:5$$

$$K_c = \frac{c_G^g c_H^h}{c_A^a c_B^b}, \qquad\qquad 8:6$$

in which a, b, g, and h are the coefficients in equation 8:5.

Equations 8:2 and 8:6 are true only for ideal solutions, but the deviations are small for solutions of nonelectrolytes or weak electrolytes.

It is evident that if the equation for a reaction is reversed the new equilibrium constant is the reciprocal of the original equilibrium constant.

Equilibrium Constant K_p. It is possible to express the equilibrium constant in terms of partial pressures as well as in terms of concentrations. Since:

$$p = \frac{n}{v} RT = cRT,$$

it is clear that $p \propto c$ and equation 8:6 can be rewritten:

$$K_p = \frac{p_G^g p_H^h}{p_A^a p_B^b}, \qquad\qquad 8:7$$

in which: p = partial pressure at equilibrium of substance indicated by subscript,

K_p = equilibrium constant in terms of partial pressures.

Equation 8:7 is applicable only to perfect gases. In this book partial pressures are given in atmospheres unless otherwise specified.

Relationship between K_p and K_c. Since:

$$c = \frac{n}{v} = \frac{p}{RT}$$

and substituting in equation 8:6, then:

$$K_c = \frac{c_G{}^g c_H{}^h}{c_A{}^a c_B{}^b} = \frac{\left(\dfrac{p_G}{RT}\right)^g \left(\dfrac{p_H}{RT}\right)^h}{\left(\dfrac{p_A}{RT}\right)^a \left(\dfrac{p_B}{RT}\right)^b}$$

$$= \frac{p_G{}^g p_H{}^h}{p_A{}^a p_B{}^b}\left(\frac{1}{RT}\right)^{(g+h)-(a+b)} = K_p\left(\frac{1}{RT}\right)^{\Delta n}$$

or:
$$K_p = K_c(RT)^{\Delta n}, \qquad\qquad \textbf{8:8}$$

in which $\Delta n = (g + h) - (a + b) =$ moles of gaseous products minus moles of gaseous reactants.

Example. At 250° C. for the reaction:

$$PCl_{5g} \rightleftarrows PCl_{3g} + Cl_{2g}$$

$K_c = 0.0414.$ Calculate K_p.
$K_p = K_c(RT)^{\Delta n} = (0.0414)[(0.0820)(523)]^{2-1}$
$\quad = 1.78.$

Equilibria Involving Gases

It is frequently desirable to know the relationships among K_p, the degree of dissociation α, and the total pressure P. Consider the following reaction:

$$N_2O_{4(g)} \rightleftarrows 2\,NO_{2(g)}.$$

If one mole of N_2O_4 is present initially, at equilibrium there will be 2α moles of NO_2 and $1 - \alpha$ moles of N_2O_4, or a total number of moles equal to $1 + \alpha$. Since partial pressure equals mole fraction times total pressure, then:

$$p_{N_2O_4} = \frac{1 - \alpha}{1 + \alpha}\,P \quad \text{and} \quad p_{NO_2} = \frac{2\alpha}{1 + \alpha}\,P.$$

Note. If an initial amount of N_2O_4 other than one mole were taken, the above equations would be unaltered because numerator and denominator would be multiplied by the same factor.

Thus:

$$K_p = \frac{p_{NO_2}{}^2}{p_{N_2O_4}} = \frac{\left(\dfrac{2\alpha}{1 + \alpha}\,P\right)^2}{\dfrac{1 - \alpha}{1 + \alpha}\,P} = \frac{4\alpha^2 P}{1 - \alpha^2}.$$

Example. At 35° C. and 1 atm., N_2O_4 is 27.0% dissociated. Calculate K_p.

$$K_p = \frac{4\alpha^2 P}{1 - \alpha^2} = \frac{(4)(0.270)^2(1)}{1 - (0.270)^2} = 0.314.$$

Consider the reaction:

$$PCl_{5_g} \rightleftarrows PCl_{3_g} + Cl_{2_g}.$$
$$1 - \alpha \qquad \alpha \qquad \alpha$$

$$p_{PCl_5} = \frac{1 - \alpha}{1 + \alpha} P; \quad p_{PCl_3} = \frac{\alpha}{1 + \alpha} P; \quad p_{Cl_2} = \frac{\alpha}{1 + \alpha} P.$$

$$K_p = \frac{p_{PCl_3} p_{Cl_2}}{p_{PCl_5}} = \frac{\left(\dfrac{\alpha}{1 + \alpha} P\right)\left(\dfrac{\alpha}{1 + \alpha} P\right)}{\left(\dfrac{1 - \alpha}{1 + \alpha} P\right)} = \frac{\alpha^2 P}{1 - \alpha^2}$$

Example. At 250° C. and 1 atm., K_p for the above reaction is 1.78. Calculate α.

$$K_p = 1.78 = \frac{(\alpha)^2(1)}{1 - \alpha^2}.$$
$$\alpha = 0.80.$$

The Le Châtelier Principle

According to Le Châtelier's principle, if a stress is brought to bear on a system in equilibrium, the system will adjust itself so as to diminish the applied stress. This principle is useful in predicting the effects of changes in temperature, pressure, and concentration on a system. Consider the following reaction:

$$N_{2_g} + 3 H_{2_g} \rightleftarrows 2 NH_{3_g}. \qquad \Delta H = -22 \text{ kcal.}$$

Since the reaction is exothermic, an increase in temperature will displace the reaction to the left and less NH_3 will be formed. An increase in the amounts of reactants will displace the reaction to the right and vice versa. Thus if some NH_3 is initially present, it will inhibit the formation of more NH_3.

Heterogeneous Chemical Equilibria

The equilibria described above are homogeneous chemical equilibria. However, if one or more solid phases are present in addition to the gaseous phase, the equilibrium in question is heterogeneous. Consider the following reaction:

$$CaCO_{3_s} \rightleftarrows CaO_s + CO_{2_g}.$$

The equilibrium constant could be written:

$$K_p' = \frac{p_{CaO} p_{CO_2}}{p_{CaCO_3}}.$$

However, the partial pressure of solid CaO and solid $CaCO_3$ is independent of the amount present and hence is a constant at a given temperature. Therefore these constants can be incorporated into K_p as follows:

$$K_p = \frac{K_p' \, p_{CaCO_3}}{p_{CaO}} = p_{CO_2}.$$

This simplification is always adopted when dealing with a heterogeneous equilibrium.

Example.   (a) NH_4HS dissociates as follows:

$$NH_4HS_s \rightleftarrows NH_{3g} + H_2S_g.$$

The equilibrium pressure at 25° C. is 0.660 atm. Calculate K_p.

$$\text{Total pressure} = p_{NH_4HS} + p_{NH_3} + p_{H_2S}$$
$$= p_{NH_3} + p_{H_2S}$$
$$\text{(since } p_{NH_4HS} \text{ is negligible)}$$
$$= 0.660.$$

Since NH_3 and H_2S are produced in the molar ratio of 1:1:

$$p_{NH_3} = p_{H_2S} = \tfrac{1}{2}(0.660) = 0.330.$$
$$K_p = p_{NH_3} \cdot p_{H_2S} = (0.330)^2$$
$$= 0.109.$$

(b) Calculate the pressure of H_2S if the above reaction takes place in a vessel originally containing NH_3 at a pressure of 0.100 atm.

$$K_p = 0.109 = (x + 0.100)(x).$$
$$x = 0.28 \text{ atm.}$$

Free-Energy Change and Equilibrium Constants

The equilibrium constant of a reaction can be calculated from the change in free energy.

Free-Energy Change and K_p. It can be shown that, for the reaction involving ideal gases:

$$aA + bB \rightleftarrows gG + hH,$$

$$\Delta F = -RT \ln K_p + RT \ln \frac{\bar{p}_G{}^g \bar{p}_H{}^h}{\bar{p}_A{}^a \bar{p}_B{}^b}, \qquad \textbf{8:9}$$

$$\Delta F = -RT \ln K_p + RT \ln Q_p, \qquad \textbf{8:10}$$

in which $\bar{p}$ refers to the arbitrary partial pressures of reactants and products as stated in the problem. If reactants in their standard states ($p = 1$ atm. for gases) are converted into products in their standard states, $Q_p = 1$ and $\ln Q_p = 0$. For this special case ΔF^0 replaces ΔF and:

$$\Delta F^0 = -RT \ln K_p, \qquad \qquad \textbf{8:11}$$

in which $\Delta F^0 =$ standard free-energy change.

Example. $\Delta F^0 = 1160$ cal. at 25° C. for the following reaction:

$$N_2O_{4_g} \rightleftarrows 2 \; NO_{2_g}.$$

Calculate K_p.

$$\Delta F^0 = -2.30 \; RT \log K_p.$$
$$1160 = -(2.30)(1.99)(298) \log K_p$$
$$K_p = 0.141.$$

Example. Calculate ΔF at 25° C. if 1 mole of N_2O_4 at 10.0 atm. is changed into 2 moles of NO_2 at 1.00 atm.

$$\Delta F = -RT \ln K_p + RT \ln Q_p$$
$$= +1160 + (2.30)(1.99)(298) \log \frac{(1.00)^2}{10.0}$$
$$= +1160 - 1360 = -200 \text{ cal.}$$

Note that the process in the first example is not spontaneous but that the process in the second example is spontaneous due to the changed conditions.

Free-Energy Change and K_c. Equations analogous to 8:9, 8:10, and 8:11 can be developed in which partial pressures are replaced by concentrations, provided the solutions are ideal.

$$\Delta F = -RT \ln K_c + RT \ln \frac{\bar{c}_G{}^g \bar{c}_H{}^h}{\bar{c}_A{}^a \bar{c}_B{}^b}, \qquad \textbf{8:12}$$

$$\Delta F = -RT \ln K_c + RT \ln Q_c, \qquad \textbf{8:13}$$

in which $\bar{c}$ refers to the arbitary concentrations of reactants and products as stated in the problem. If reactants in their standard state (molarity = 1) are converted into products in their standard state, $Q_c = 1$ and $\ln Q_c = 0$. For this special case ΔF^0 replaces ΔF and:

$$\Delta F^0 = -RT \ln K_c. \qquad \textbf{8:14}$$

Standard Free Energies of Formation. Standard free-energy changes are additive. Tables of standard free energies of formation may be tabulated in a manner analogous to the heats of formation. See Table 8 (p. 82). The free energies of elements in their most stable form at 25° C. and 1 atm. are arbitrarily assigned the value of zero. It is possible to calculate ΔF^0 (and the equilibrium constant with the aid of equations 8:11 and 8:14) for various reactions with the aid of such a table.

TABLE 8
STANDARD FREE ENERGIES OF FORMATION AT 25° C. AND 1 ATM.

Substance	ΔF^0 in cal./mole
H_2O_l	$-56,560$
H_2O_g	$-54,507$
HCl_g	$-22,692$
HBr_g	$-12,540$
HI_g	315
NH_{3_g}	$-3,910$
CO_g	$-32,700$
CO_{2_g}	$-94,100$
CH_{4_g}	$-12,085$
$C_2H_{6_g}$	$-7,787$
$C_2H_5OH_l$	$-40,200$
$C_6H_{6_l}$	$29,400$

Example. Calculate ΔF^0 for the following reaction at 25° C. and 1 atm.

$$Cl_{2_g} + 2\ HI_g \rightarrow 2\ HCl_g + I_{2_g}.$$

$$\Delta F^0 = \Delta F^0_{products} - \Delta F^0_{reactants}$$
$$= [(2)(-22692) + 0] - [0 + (2)(315)]$$
$$= -46014\ \text{cal.}$$

The Equilibrium Constant as a Function of Temperature

From the second law of thermodynamics, it is possible to derive the Gibbs-Helmholz equation:

$$\frac{\Delta H^0 - \Delta F^0}{T} = -\frac{d\Delta F^0}{dT}, \qquad 8:15$$

in which $\dfrac{d\Delta F^0}{dT}$ represents the rate of change of ΔF^0 with temperature. Differentiating equation 8:11 with respect to temperature:

$$-\frac{d\Delta F^0}{dT} = R \ln K_p + RT \frac{d \ln K_p}{dT} \qquad 8:16$$

and substituting in equation 8:15:

$$\frac{\Delta H^0 - \Delta F^0}{T} = R \ln K_p + RT \frac{d \ln K_p}{dT} \qquad 8:17$$

or:

$$\Delta H^0 - \Delta F^0 = RT \ln K_p + RT^2 \frac{d \ln K_p}{dT}. \qquad 8:18$$

Adding equation 8:11 to equation 8:18:

$$\Delta H^0 = RT^2 \frac{d \ln K_p}{dT}. \qquad\qquad \textbf{8:19}$$

Since ΔH changes very little with a change in pressure:

$$\Delta H \cong \Delta H^0. \qquad\qquad \textbf{8:20}$$

Then:
$$d \ln K_p = \frac{\Delta H}{RT^2} dT. \qquad\qquad \textbf{8:21}$$

If the temperature range is small (or if the heat capacities of reactants and products are about the same) equation 8:21 may be integrated as follows:

$$\int d \ln K_p = \frac{\Delta H}{R} \int \frac{dT}{T^2}. \qquad\qquad \textbf{8:22}$$

$$\ln K_p = -\frac{\Delta H}{R} \frac{1}{T} + C. \qquad\qquad \textbf{8:23}$$

If $\log K_p$ is plotted versus $\frac{1}{T}$, a straight line is obtained for which:

$$\text{slope} = -\frac{\Delta H}{2.303R}. \qquad\qquad \textbf{8:24}$$

However, equation 8:22 may be integrated between limits in a manner similar to that used for the Clausius-Clapeyron equation:

$$\int_{K_{p_1}}^{K_{p_2}} d \ln K_p = \frac{\Delta H}{R} \int_{T_1}^{T_2} \frac{dT}{T^2}. \qquad\qquad \textbf{8:25}$$

Then:
$$\log \frac{K_{p_2}}{K_{p_1}} = \frac{\Delta H(T_2 - T_1)}{2.303RT_2T_1}, \qquad\qquad \textbf{8:26}$$

in which: K_{p_2} = equilibrium constant at T_2,
K_{p_1} = equilibrium constant at T_1.

If K_p is known at two temperatures, K_p at some other temperature can be determined graphically with the aid of equation 8:23 or by substitution into equation 8:26 (after first calculating ΔH).

An equation using K_c analogous to equation 8:26 can be derived, but in this case ΔE replaces ΔH, i.e.:

$$\log \frac{K_{c_2}}{K_{c_1}} = \frac{\Delta E(T_2 - T_1)}{2.303RT_2T_1}. \qquad\qquad \textbf{8:27}$$

Example. For the reaction:

$$N_2O_{4g} \rightleftarrows 2\ NO_{2g}$$
$$\Delta H = 14,600 \text{ cal.}$$

If $K_p = 0.141$ at 298° K., calculate K_p at 338° K.

$$\log \frac{K_p}{0.141} = \frac{(14600)(338 - 298)}{(2.30)(1.99)(338)(298)}.$$
$$\log K_p = 0.419.$$
$$K_p = 2.62.$$

Calculation of ΔF^0 from Thermal Data

It is possible to calculate ΔH^0 for a chemical reaction by the methods discussed in Chapter 6. Further, it is possible to determine the absolute entropies of elements and compounds by application of the third law of thermodynamics. Then, for a chemical reaction:

$$\Delta S^0 = S^0_{products} - S^0_{reactants}.$$

From such data (based entirely on thermal measurements) it is possible to calculate ΔF^0 by substitution in equation 6:28 (from Chapter 6), $\Delta F^0 = \Delta H^0 - T\Delta S^0$.

Example. For the reaction:

$$C_{(graphite)} + 2\ H_{2(g)} \rightarrow CH_{4(g)}$$

at 25° C., $\Delta H^0 = -17,900$ cal./mole. The absolute entropies, S^0, in calories per degree-mole at 25° C. for graphite, hydrogen, and methane are, respectively, 1.40, 31.2, and 44.4. Calculate ΔF^0 at 25° C. for this reaction.

$$\begin{aligned}
\Delta S^0 &= S^0_{products} - S^0_{reactants} \\
&= 44.4 - [1.40 + 2(31.2)] \\
&= 44.4 - 63.8 = -19.4. \\
\Delta F^0 &= \Delta H^0 - T\Delta S^0 \\
&= -17900 - [(298)(-19.4)] \\
&= -12100 \text{ cal./mole (to three significant figures).}
\end{aligned}$$

The Distribution Law

If a solute is added to a system containing two immiscible liquids, the solute will distribute itself between the two layers in a definite manner. The ratio of the concentrations in the two liquids is a constant called the *distribution coefficient*, K_D, or:

$$K_D = \frac{c_2}{c_1}, \qquad \qquad \textbf{8:28}$$

in which: c_2 = concentration of solute in solvent 2,
c_1 = concentration of solute in solvent 1.

However, if the solute dimerizes in one liquid but not in the other the equilibrium can be written:

$$A_2 \rightleftarrows 2\,A$$

and:

$$K_D = \frac{c_A{}^2}{c_{A_2}}$$

8:29

An example is the distribution of benzoic acid between chloroform and water. The benzoic acid exists as a monomer in water and as a dimer in chloroform.

Review Questions and Problems

1. Starting with the law of mass action, derive equation 8:6.
2. State the Le Châtelier principle.
3. State the influence of an increase in temperature on the following reactions:

$$\begin{array}{ll} N_2 + O_2 \rightleftarrows 2\,NO & \text{endothermic} \\ 2\,SO_2 + O_2 \rightleftarrows 2\,SO_3 & \text{exothermic} \\ PCl_5 \rightleftarrows PCl_3 + Cl_2 & \text{endothermic} \end{array}$$

4. Assuming all the substances involved are gases, state the effect of an increase in pressure on the reactions in Problem 3.
5. Describe the effect on dissociation of introducing one of the products.
6. For the reaction:

$$2\,A_g + B_g \rightleftarrows A_2 B_g,$$

if two moles of A are mixed with one mole of B and allowed to come to equilibrium at 100° C. in a 1-liter flask, 0.5 mole of A_2B is formed. Calculate K_c and K_p at 100° C.

7. At 25° C. for the reaction:

$$A_{2_g} \rightleftarrows 2\,A_g$$

$K_c = 0.165$. If one mole of A_2 is placed in a 0.1-liter flask at 25° C., calculate how many moles of A are formed at equilibrium.

8. Calculate ΔF^0 for the reaction in Problem 7.
9. For a certain reaction, $K_p = 1.21 \times 10^{-4}$ at 1800° K. and 2.31×10^{-4} at 1900° K. Calculate K_p at 2000° K.
10. For the reaction:

$$A_s \rightleftarrows 2\,B_g + C_g$$

express K_p as a function of the total pressure, P.

9

The Phase Rule and Phase Equilibria

A phase is a homogeneous, physically distinct part of a system, separated from other parts by definite boundaries. Thus for instance, water, ice, and vapor constitute three separate phases of a system.

The Phase Rule

According to the phase rule (derived by J. Willard Gibbs in 1876):

$$F = C - P + 2, \qquad \textbf{9:1}$$

in which:
F = number of degrees of freedom,
C = number of components,
P = number of phases.

The number of phases, P, is the number of physically distinct states (i.e., solid, liquid, or gas) which exist in a system at equilibrium. Only one gaseous phase is possible since all gases are miscible with each other. Several solid and several liquid phases are possible in one system. For example, a system containing solid sulfur, water, and kerosene would contain three phases.

The number of components, C, is the smallest number of chemical constituents which must be specified in order to express the composition of every phase present in the system.

The number of degrees of freedom, F, is the number of variable factors (temperature, pressure, and concentration) which must be specified in order that the condition of a system at equilibrium be defined completely.

Phase Diagrams

A phase diagram gives the equilibrium conditions between the various phases present in a system.

One-Component Systems. Since in a one-component system, concentration is not a variable, the phase diagram may be represented by a plot of pressure versus temperature.

THE WATER SYSTEM.   The pressure-temperature diagram for water is shown in Fig. 24.   It is not drawn to scale because of the large range of pressures involved.

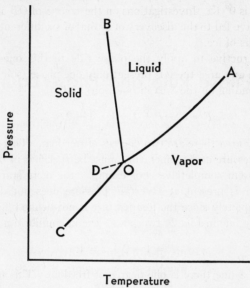

Fig. 24.

Vapor, liquid, and solid exist in the areas so indicated in the diagram.

The line *OA* represents the vapor-pressure curve of water. Above this line only liquid water exists, and below this line only water vapor exists. However, along the line *OA* liquid water and water vapor are in equilibrium.

The line *OC* represents the sublimation curve of ice. Above *OC* only ice exists, and below *OC* only water vapor exists. Along *OC* both ice and water vapor exist in equilibrium.

The line *OB* represents the effect of pressure on the melting point of ice. Since the line *OB* slopes to the left, it is clear that the melting point of ice decreases as the pressure increases. Along *OB* ice and liquid water are in equilibrium.

The dotted line *OD* is an extension of *OA* and represents the vapor pressure of supercooled water. Such dotted lines are used in phase diagrams to indicate less stable equilibria. These are known as *metastable equilibria.*

At the point *O*, solid, liquid, and vapor are in equilibrium with each other. A point at which three phases are in equilibrium is called a *triple point*.

The line OA stops at the critical temperature. The theoretical limit of OC is $0°$ K. Investigations on the course of OB at very high pressures have led to the discovery of a total of six different crystalline modifications of ice.

It is instructive to apply the phase rule to this one-component system. In any area there is present only one phase (solid, liquid, or vapor, depending on the area in question) and:

$$F = C - P + 2 = 1 - 1 + 2 = 2.$$

Thus in any area there are two degrees of freedom. This means that both the pressure and temperature must be specified in order to define the system completely. For example, the mere statement that water vapor is present at a certain pressure does not describe the system completely since the temperature is not defined.

Along any line in Fig. 24 two phases are in equilibrium and:

$$F = 1 - 2 + 2 = 1.$$

Thus along a line there is one degree of freedom. This implies that along a line the pressure is automatically fixed if the temperature is stated and that the temperature is automatically fixed if the pressure is stated. For example, along OA liquid water and water vapor are in equilibrium. If it is stated that liquid water and water vapor are in equilibrium at a given temperature, the pressure is automatically fixed and can be read from the curve OA. Further, if it is stated that liquid water and water vapor are in equilibrium under a given vapor pressure the temperature must be that indicated by the curve OA. Similar considerations apply to any line in Fig. 24.

At a triple point there are three phases in equilibrium and:

$$F = 1 - 3 + 2 = 0.$$

This implies that at a triple point both the pressure and the temperature are automatically fixed. For example, if it is stated that liquid water, ice, and water vapor are in equilibrium, then the temperature and pressure are automatically fixed since they must correspond to point O in Fig. 24. For H_2O, the triple point corresponds to a pressure of 4.58 mm. and a temperature of 0.0098° C.

THE SULFUR SYSTEM. The sulfur system is a somewhat more complicated one since two solid phases (rhombic and monoclinic) as well as liquid and vapor exist. The pressure-temperature diagram for sulfur is shown in Fig. 25 (again, not to scale).

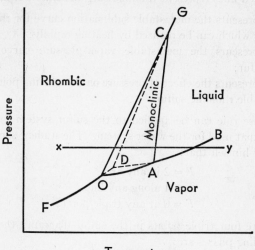

Fig. 25.

OF   represents the sublimation curve of rhombic sulfur;

OA   represents the sublimation curve of monoclinic sulfur;

AB   represents the vapor-pressure curve of liquid sulfur;

OC   represents the effect of pressure on the transition temperature between rhombic and monoclinic sulfur;

AC   represents the effect of pressure on the melting point of monoclinic sulfur;

CG   represents the effect of pressure on the melting point of rhombic sulfur.

If rhombic sulfur at a pressure and temperature corresponding to point *x* in Fig. 25 is heated slowly at constant pressure (i.e., along the line *xy*), the rhombic sulfur will change to monoclinic sulfur at the temperature corresponding to the intersection of *xy* with *OC*. The monoclinic sulfur will melt at the temperature corresponding to the intersection of *xy* with *AC*. The liquid sulfur will boil at the temperature corresponding to the intersection of *xy* with *AB*.

However, if rhombic sulfur at *x* is heated rapidly along *xy*, there is not sufficient time for the transition from rhombic to monoclinic to take place at the intersection of *xy* and *OC*. In this case, the metastable rhombic sulfur will melt at a temperature corresponding to the intersection of xy with DC.

The dotted lines represent the following metastable equilibria:

OD represents the metastable sublimation curve for rhombic sulfur which can be realized by heating rapidly;

DA represents the metastable vapor-pressure curve of liquid sulfur;

DC represents the effect of pressure on the melting point of metastable rhombic sulfur.

The phase rule can be applied to the sulfur system in a manner similar to that used for the water system. The student should do this and satisfy himself that:

$$F = 2 \text{ in any area,}$$
$$F = 1 \text{ along any line,}$$
$$F = 0 \text{ at any triple point.}$$

There are four triple points in the sulfur diagram; these and the corresponding phases are:

O: rhombic, monoclinic, and vapor;
D: rhombic, liquid, and vapor (metastable);
A: monoclinic, liquid, and vapor;
C: rhombic, monoclinic, and liquid.

Two-Component Systems. For a two-component system, F is greatest when $P = 1$. Then:

$$F = C - P + 2 = 2 - 1 + 2 = 3.$$

Thus three variables must be specified in order to describe the system — pressure, temperature, and the concentration of one of the components. A set of three co-ordinate axes at right angles to each other would be required to represent these relations graphically. However, it is the practice to disregard the vapor phase and to fix an arbitrary pressure of 1 atm. The experimental work is then done in open vessels at 1 atm. Of course, the pressure under these conditions is not the equilibrium value, but for solid-liquid equilibria the effect of pressure is negligible. Thus, the results obtained are substantially the same as if the system were in true equilibrium with its vapor. A *condensed system* is one in which only solid and liquid phases are considered. If the pressure is kept constant (and this is assumed in all subsequent discussion of two-component systems), then:

$$F = C - P + 1.$$

Simple Eutectic Diagram. For a two-component system at constant pressure in which one phase is present:

$$F = 2 - 1 + 1 = 2.$$

Since $F = 2$, only two variables must be specified in order to describe the system, and thus the equilibrium can be represented in two dimensions by means of a temperature-composition diagram, an example of which is shown in Fig. 26.

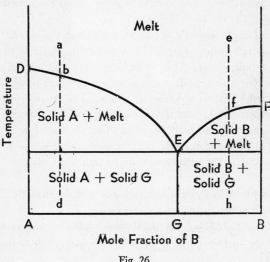

Fig. 26.

Point D represents the melting point of pure A, and F represents the melting point of pure B. It is seen that the addition of B to A lowers the melting point as does the addition of A to B. The curves DE and EF represent the melting points of various mixtures of A and B.

Consider melt of composition corresponding to a which is cooled. At a temperature corresponding to b, solid A separates out and the melt remaining is relatively richer in B. On further cooling, solid A continues to separate out until a temperature corresponding to E is reached. At this temperature, another solid phase, G (a mixture of solid A and solid B), appears and G continues to solidify until the remaining melt is completely solidified. Then nothing but a mixture of solid A and solid G remains, which can be cooled further. Of course, the *over-all* composition has remained the same, as indicated by the dotted line *abd*.

Along the curve DE solid A and melt are in equilibrium, and hence $F = 2 - 2 + 1 = 1$. Thus specification of either the temperature or the composition serves to define the system completely.

At E, there are three phases in equilibrium: solid A, solid G, and melt, and hence $F = 2 - 3 + 1 = 0$. Thus if it is stated that solid A, solid G, and melt are in equilibrium, the temperature and composition are automatically fixed and must correspond to E. The temperature at E represents the lowest temperature at which a liquid phase can exist in this system. This temperature is called the *eutectic tempera- ture* and point E is called the *eutectic point*.

If melt of composition e is cooled, solid B separates out at a tem- perature corresponding to f and the remaining melt is richer in A. On further cooling, solid B continues to separate out until E is reached. At E, solid G separates out at constant temperature until all the melt has solidified. Then only solid B and solid G remain; they can be cooled further. Of course the *over-all* composition remains constant. Along EF, solid B and melt are in equilibrium, and $F = 1$.

Above DEF, only melt is present and $F = 2 - 1 + 1 = 2$. The phases present in the other areas are as indicated, and in these areas $F = 1$.

An example of a system exhibiting a simple eutectic diagram is bismuth-cadmium.

THERMAL ANALYSIS. Temperature-composition diagrams such as that in Fig. 26 can be constructed from temperature-time curves. See Fig. 27.

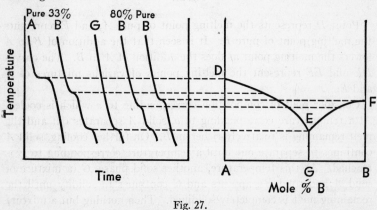

Fig. 27.

If pure liquid A is cooled, a horizontal portion in the temperature- time curve is obtained which corresponds to the melting point of pure A. If liquid containing 33 mole % B in A is cooled, two breaks in the temperature-time curve are obtained. The first break corresponds to the temperature at which solid A starts to separate out, and the second break corresponds to the eutectic temperature. If liquid of composition G is cooled, only one break in the temperature-time curve is obtained. This occurs at the eutectic temperature. If liquid containing 80 mole % B is cooled, two breaks are obtained. The first corresponds to the temperature at which solid B starts to separate out, and the second to the eutectic temperature. If pure liquid B is cooled, only one break is obtained. This corresponds to the melting point of pure B. These temperature-time data are then converted into a temperature-composition curve as shown in Fig. 27. This method is called *thermal analysis*.

COMPOUND FORMATION. A maximum obtained in the temperature-composition curve, such as the one in Fig. 28, indicates the formation of a compound.

Since Fig. 28 can be considered to be two simple eutectic diagrams placed side by side, no essentially new considerations are involved. However, G represents the melting point of the compound AB.

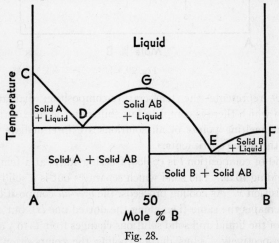

Fig. 28.

D represents the eutectic between A and AB, and E represents the eutectic between AB and B. The formula of the compound is determined by the composition corresponding to the maximum. Since in Fig. 28 the maximum comes at 50 mole % B, the formula is AB. An example of a system of this type is KCl and $CaCl_2$; the formula of the compound formed is $KCl \cdot CaCl_2$. If the maximum had come at 66.7 mole % B the formula of the compound would be AB_2. In some systems, several maxima are known, and each corresponds to a stable compound.

SOLID SOLUTIONS. In the two-component systems discussed so far, only pure substances have separated on cooling of the liquid phase. However, in some cases the solid which separates out is found to contain both components in continuously changing proportions.

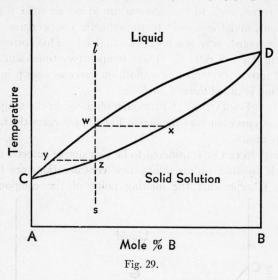

Fig. 29.

Fig. 29 represents the temperature-composition diagram for a system in which there is complete miscibility in the solid state and in which the melting points of all solutions are intermediate between those of the pure constituents.

If liquid of composition l is cooled, freezing starts at a temperature corresponding to w. The solid which separates out is a solid solution of composition x. As cooling proceeds, the *over-all* composition of the system remains the same (i.e., along the dotted line ls), but the composition of the liquid and solid solutions changes from w to y and from x to z respectively. Thus during cooling the composition of both liquid and solid phases must change continuously. At a temperature corresponding to y, the last drop of liquid freezes, and the solid remaining has the same composition as that of the original liquid. The upper curve of Fig. 29 is called the *liquidus curve*, and the lower curve is called the *solidus curve*.

In the areas labeled "Liquid" and "Solid Solution" only one phase is present, and $F = 2 - 1 + 1 = 2$. In the area enclosed by the two curves, two phases are in equilibrium, and $F = 2 - 2 + 1 = 1$. There is no point in a diagram of this type at which $F = 0$. An example of a system of this type is AgCl-NaCl.

Some temperature-composition diagrams involving solid solutions show maxima or minima. They are analogous to the boiling-point curves shown in Figs. 21 and 22.

PARTIAL MISCIBILITY. A system in which the two components are partially miscible in the liquid state is shown in Fig. 30.

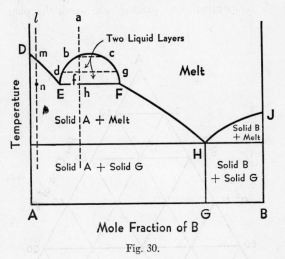

Fig. 30.

The typical partial-miscibility diagram consists of a simple eutectic type of diagram with an area of partial miscibility of the melt superimposed upon it. As melt of composition a, lying between E and F, is cooled, a second liquid layer of composition c appears at a temperature corresponding to b. Further cooling changes the composition of the two liquid layers as well as the relative amounts of the two layers. At a temperature corresponding to f, two liquid layers of compositions d and g are in equilibrium. At a temperature corresponding to h, solid A begins to deposit as follows:

$$\text{Liquid } E \rightarrow \text{Solid } A + \text{Liquid } F.$$

Since three phases are present at this point, $F = 0$, and the temperature will remain constant until all of liquid E has been consumed. Further cooling can then take place. That part of the diagram below the line EF has already been discussed under the simple eutectic type.

If melt of composition *l* is cooled, solid *A* will start to separate out at a temperature corresponding to *m*. On further cooling, solid *A* will continue to separate out until a temperature corresponding to *n* is reached. At this temperature the melt will separate into two liquid phases, *E* and *F*. The temperature will remain constant until all of liquid *E* has been converted to solid *A* and liquid *F*, after which further cooling can take place.

An example of a system of this type is phenol-water.

Three-Component Systems. For a three-component system in which both temperature and pressure are fixed, the phase rule becomes:

$$F = C - P = 3 - P.$$

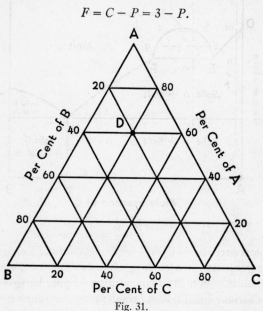

Fig. 31.

Three-component systems at fixed temperature and pressure may be conveniently represented by an equilateral triangle. See Fig. 31. The three components are designated as *A*, *B*, and *C*. Each vertex of the triangle represents 100 per cent of the component indicated. The opposite base line represents 0 per cent of the given component. A point within the diagram represents a mixture of *A*, *B*, and *C*. For example, in Fig. 31, point *D* represents a mixture of 60% *A*, 20% *B*, and 20% *C*. Point *D* represents 60% *A* since this point is 60% of the distance from the base *BC* towards the vertex *A*. Similar considerations apply to *B* and *C*.

Fig. 32 shows a system of three liquids with one partially miscible pair. If a small amount of C is added to pure B a homogeneous solu-

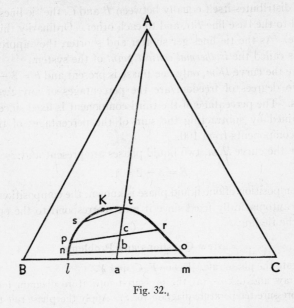

Fig. 32.

tion is formed. If more C is added the solution becomes saturated at the composition represented by l. If more C is added, the mixture will separate into two layers, one of which consists of B saturated with C and the other of which consists of C saturated with B. The composition of the two layers is represented by l and m. As more C is added the relative amounts of the two layers l and m change. When the over-all composition of the mixture reaches m, liquid layer l disappears and only a single homogeneous liquid remains.

A mixture of B and C with an over-all composition given by a consists of two layers of composition l and m. The addition of A increases the solubility of B in C and also of C in B. If enough A is added so that the composition of the system corresponds to b, then two layers will be present whose compositions correspond to n and o. Both n and o represent solutions containing A, B, and C. The line joining n and o is called a *tie line*.

If more A is added so that the composition of the system corresponds to c, the two layers in equilibrium will have the compositions p and r. If enough A is added to bring the composition of the system to t, two layers with compositions of s and t will be present. If still more

A is added, layer s will disappear and the system will consist of a single homogeneous liquid.

If A distributes itself equally between B and C, the tie lines will be parallel to the base line BC, and to each other. Ordinarily this is not the case. As the tie lines get shorter and shorter, they approach K, which is called the *isothermal critical point* of the system.

Above the curve lKm, only one phase is present and $F = 3 - 1 = 2$. The two degrees of freedom are the percentages of any two components. The percentage of the third component is fixed since it can be obtained by subtracting the sum of the percentages of the two known components from 100.

Below the curve lKm, two liquid phases are present and:

$$F = 3 - 2 = 1.$$

If the composition of one liquid phase is known, the composition of the other is automatically fixed since it must correspond to the opposite end of the tie line.

Review Questions and Problems

1. State the phase rule. Define F, C, and P.
2. Draw and discuss (a) the pressure-temperature diagram for H_2O; (b) the pressure-temperature diagram for S. Apply the phase rule to both diagrams.
3. What is a triple point? Illustrate with reference to S.
4. What is a metastable equilibrium? Illustrate with reference to H_2O.
5. Draw and discuss a simple eutectic diagram.
6. Draw and discuss a phase diagram in which a stable compound is formed.
7. Draw and discuss a phase diagram in which a continuous series of solid solutions is formed.
8. Explain how a temperature-composition diagram can be constructed by the method of thermal analysis.
9. Sketch the general form of the phase diagram for a system of two components having the following properties:

melting point of $A = 300°$ C.
melting point of $B = 200°$ C.
melting point of $AB_2 = 400°$ C.
eutectic of A and $AB_2 = 250°$ C.
eutectic of AB_2 and $B = 150°$ C.

10. Draw and discuss a phase diagram for a two-component system which exhibits partial miscibility in the liquid state.
11. Draw and discuss a phase diagram for a three-component system in which one pair of liquids is partially miscible.

10

Chemical Kinetics

Chemical kinetics is concerned not only with the velocity of reactions but also with the intermediate steps by which reactants are ultimately converted into products.

Molecularity of Reactions

A *unimolecular* reaction is one in which only one molecule reacts at a time. Examples are:

$$Br_2 \rightarrow Br + Br.$$

$$\begin{array}{ccc} H-C-COOH & & H-C-COOH \\ \| & \rightarrow & \| \\ H-C-COOH & & HOOC-C-H. \end{array}$$

A *bimolecular* reaction is one in which two molecules (either of the same or of different kinds) react. Examples are:

$$H_2 + Br_2 \rightarrow 2\ HBr.$$
$$2\ HI \rightarrow H_2 + I_2.$$

A *termolecular* reaction takes place as a result of the simultaneous collision of three molecules. An example is:

$$2\ NO + O_2 \rightarrow 2\ NO_2.$$

First-Order Reactions

A first-order reaction is one in which the rate of the reaction is found by experiment to be directly proportional to the concentration of the reacting substance. It follows from the law of mass action that at constant volume:

$$-\frac{dc}{dt} = kc, \qquad \textbf{10:1}$$

in which: c = concentration of reactant,

   t = time,

   k = constant (called the *rate constant*),

   $-\dfrac{dc}{dt}$ = rate of decrease in concentration with time.

Rearranging and integrating:

$$-\int \frac{dc}{c} = k \int dt. \qquad \textbf{10:2}$$

$$-\ln c = kt + \text{constant}.$$

$$\log c = \frac{-k}{2.303} t - \frac{\text{constant}}{2.303}. \qquad \textbf{10:3}$$

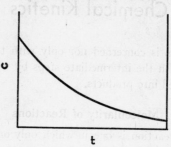

Fig. 33.

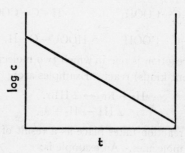

Fig. 34.

Thus, if $\log c$ is plotted versus t, a straight line is obtained whose slope is $-k/2.303$. See Figs. 33 and 34. However, if equation 10:2 is integrated between the limits, c_1 at t_1 and c_2 at t_2:

$$-\int_{c_1}^{c_2} \frac{dc}{c} = k \int_{t_1}^{t_2} dt. \qquad \textbf{10:4}$$

$$-\ln \frac{c_2}{c_1} = k(t_2 - t_1). \qquad \textbf{10:5}$$

$$\ln \frac{c_1}{c_2} = k(t_2 - t_1). \qquad \textbf{10:6}$$

$$k = \frac{2.303}{t_2 - t_1} \log \frac{c_1}{c_2}, \qquad \textbf{10:7}$$

in which: c_1 = concentration of reactant at time t_1,
              c_2 = concentration of reactant at time t_2.

Equation 10:7 can be modified as follows:

$$k = \frac{2.303}{t} \log \frac{c_0}{c},$$ **10:8**

in which: c_0 = concentration at the beginning of reaction (i.e., $t = 0$),
         c = concentration left at time t.

If the initial concentration of reactant is represented by a and the amount reacted in time t is represented by x, then $a - x$ is the concentration remaining after time t, and:

$$k = \frac{2.303}{t} \log \frac{a}{a - x}.$$ **10:9**

It is evident from equations 10:8 and 10:9 that k has the units of time^{-1} or usually sec.$^{-1}$.

The "half-life," $t_{\frac{1}{2}}$, is the time necessary for half of a given quantity of material to react. Then:

$$k = \frac{2.303}{t_{\frac{1}{2}}} \log \frac{1}{\frac{1}{2}}$$ **10:10**

or: $$t_{\frac{1}{2}} = \frac{0.693}{k}.$$ **10:11**

In general, if a reaction has been shown to be of first order it can be assumed to be unimolecular. A reaction is of first order if:

1. reasonably constant values for k are obtained when the experimental data are substituted into equations 10:7, 10:8, or 10:9; or
2. a straight line is obtained when log c is plotted versus t (equation 10:3).

Example. For the reaction:

$$A \rightarrow B + C$$

the following data were obtained:

t in sec.	0	900	1800
conc. of A	50.8	19.7	7.62

Prove that the reaction is of first order.

$$k = \frac{2.30}{t} \log \frac{c_0}{c}.$$

$$k = \frac{2.30}{900} \log \frac{50.8}{19.7} = 0.00105 \text{ sec.}^{-1}$$

$$k = \frac{2.30}{1800} \log \frac{50.8}{7.62} = 0.00105 \text{ sec.}^{-1}$$

Since the two values of k agree, the reaction is of first order.

Example. In the example above, calculate how long it would take for half of the original material to decompose.

$$t_{\frac{1}{2}} = \frac{0.693}{k} = \frac{0.693}{0.00105} = 660 \text{ sec.}$$

Second-Order Reactions

If the rate of a reaction depends on the concentration of two substances, the reaction is of second order. If:

$$A + B \rightarrow AB,$$

then:

$$-\frac{dc_A}{dt} = -\frac{dc_B}{dt} = kc_A c_B, \qquad \textbf{10:12}$$

in which $-\dfrac{dc_A}{dt}$ = rate at which the concentration of A decreases,

$-\dfrac{dc_B}{dt}$ = rate at which the concentration of B decreases,

$\qquad k$ = rate constant,

$\qquad c_A$ = concentration of A,

$\qquad c_B$ = concentration of B.

If the initial molar concentrations of A and B are represented by a and b respectively, and if x denotes the amount of A or B reacting in time t, then:

$$\frac{dx}{dt} = k(a - x)(b - x). \qquad \textbf{10:13}$$

However, if $a = b$, then:

$$\frac{dx}{dt} = k(a - x)^2. \qquad \textbf{10:14}$$

Integrating:

$$\int \frac{dx}{(a - x)^2} = k \int dt.$$

$$\frac{1}{a - x} = kt + C, \qquad \textbf{10:15}$$

in which C = constant of integration. The constant C may be evaluated by setting $x = 0$ when $t = 0$. Then:

$$\frac{1}{a - 0} = k(0) + C$$

or:

$$C = \frac{1}{a}. \qquad \textbf{10:16}$$

Substituting into equation 10:15:

$$\frac{1}{a-x} = kt + \frac{1}{a}.$$

$$\frac{1}{a-x} - \frac{1}{a} = kt.$$

$$\frac{a}{a(a-x)} - \frac{a-x}{a(a-x)} = kt. \qquad \textbf{10:17}$$

$$k = \frac{1}{t}\frac{x}{a(a-x)}. \qquad \textbf{10:18}$$

If concentrations are expressed in moles/liter and time is expressed in seconds, then k has the units of liters/mole-seconds.

When half of the original material has reacted, $x = a/2$ and:

$$k = \frac{1}{t_{\frac{1}{2}}}\frac{\dfrac{a}{2}}{a\left(a - \dfrac{a}{2}\right)} = \frac{1}{t_{\frac{1}{2}}}\frac{1}{a}$$

or:
$$t_{\frac{1}{2}} = \frac{1}{ka}. \qquad \textbf{10:19}$$

It must be remembered that equations 10:18 and 10:19 apply only when $a = b$.

If $a \neq b$, then equation 10:13 must be integrated. This integration gives the following equation (after evaluating the integration constant and converting to common logarithms):

$$k = \frac{2.303}{t(a-b)} \log \frac{b(a-x)}{a(b-x)}. \qquad \textbf{10:20}$$

In general, a reaction may be assumed to be bimolecular if it is of second order. A reaction is of second order if:

1. reasonably constant values of k are obtained when experimental data are substituted into equations 10:18 (if $a = b$) or 10:20 (if $a \neq b$); or
2. a straight line is obtained when $1/(a-x)$ is plotted versus time (true only if $a = b$).

An example of a second-order reaction is the saponification of ethyl acetate by sodium hydroxide:

$$CH_3COOC_2H_5 + OH^- \rightarrow CH_3COO^- + C_2H_5OH.$$

Example. A certain bimolecular reaction in which $a = b = 1$ mole/liter is 10% complete in 10 minutes. How long does it take the reaction to be 50% complete?

$$k = \frac{1}{t} \frac{x}{a(a - x)} = \frac{1}{10} \frac{0.1}{(1)(1 - 0.1)}.$$

$$k = \frac{0.1}{9} = 0.0111 \text{ liter/mole-minute.}$$

$$t_{\frac{1}{2}} = \frac{1}{ka} = \frac{1}{(0.0111)(1)} = 90 \text{ min.}$$

Third-order reactions exist, but are rare.

Zero-Order Reactions

A reaction is of zero order if the reaction rate is unaffected by concentration. This is possible if the rate is determined by some other limiting factor, as absorption of light, or if the concentration is kept constant (as in a saturated solution). For such a reaction:

$$-\frac{dc_A}{dt} = k$$

or:

$$c_A = -kt + \text{a constant,}$$

and a plot of concentration versus time yields a straight line. This criterion can be used to prove that a reaction is of zero order.

Complex Reactions

Only a few reactions are straightforward first-, second-, or third-order reactions. Instead, several reactions are usually taking place at one time. There are three important types of complications.

Consecutive Reactions. A consecutive reaction may be represented as:

$$A \xrightarrow{k_1} B \xrightarrow{k_2} C,$$

in which k_1 is the rate constant for the first step and k_2 is the rate constant for the second step. Consecutive reactions are very common. For example, the oxidation of ethane to CO_2 and H_2O really passes through a series of intermediate steps in which alcohols, ketones, acids, etc., are formed.

Reverse Reactions. A reverse reaction may be represented as:

$$A + B \underset{k_2}{\overset{k_1}{\rightleftarrows}} C + D,$$

in which k_1 is the rate constant for the forward reaction and k_2 is the rate constant for the reverse reaction. If the rate of the reverse reaction is appreciable, it must be taken into account in the evaluation of k_1 if a correct value is to be obtained.

Side Reactions. A side reaction may be represented as:

$$A \begin{array}{c} \nearrow^{k_1} B \\ \searrow_{k_2} C \end{array}$$

These are especially common in organic chemistry.   For example, the nitration of phenol gives both o-nitrophenol and p-nitrophenol.   The amounts of each isomer obtained depend on k_1 and k_2.   The organic chemist tries to suppress undesirable side reactions by appropriate control of temperature, pressure, catalyst, and other factors.

Influence of Temperature on Reaction Rates

An increase in temperature causes an increase in the rate of a chemical reaction.   The rates of many organic reactions are doubled for each $10°$ rise in temperature.

In 1889 Arrhenius proposed the following empirical equation, which gives k as a function of T:

$$k = se^{-\frac{\Delta H_a}{RT}}, \qquad\qquad \textbf{10:21}$$

in which:
$$k = \text{rate constant,}$$
$$s = \text{a constant,}$$
$$e = 2.718,$$
$$\Delta H_a = \text{constant} = \text{energy of activation,}$$
$$R = \text{molar gas constant,}$$
$$T = \text{absolute temperature.}$$

Taking logarithms of both sides:

$$\ln k = \frac{-\Delta H_a}{RT} + \ln s \qquad\qquad \textbf{10:22}$$

or:
$$2.303 \log k = \frac{-\Delta H_a}{RT} + 2.303 \log s.$$

$$\log k = \frac{-\Delta H_a}{2.303\,RT} + \log s. \qquad\qquad \textbf{10:23}$$

Thus if $\log k$ is plotted versus $1/T$, a straight line is obtained in which:

$$\text{slope} = -\frac{\Delta H_a}{(2.303)(1.987)}.$$ **10:24**

See Fig. 35.

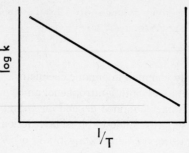

Fig. 35.

Thus equation 10:23 can be used to calculate the energy of activation graphically.

Another equation for calculating ΔH_a can be obtained as follows. Differentiating equation 10:22 with respect to temperature:

$$\frac{d \ln k}{dT} = \frac{\Delta H_a}{RT^2}.$$

Assuming that ΔH_a is constant over the temperature range in question and integrating between limits:

$$\ln \frac{k_2}{k_1} = \frac{\Delta H_a(T_2 - T_1)}{RT_2T_1}$$

or: $$\log \frac{k_2}{k_1} = \frac{\Delta H_a(T_2 - T_1)}{2.303\ RT_2T_1}.$$ **10:25**

Thus ΔH_a can be calculated if the rate constants are known for two different temperatures.

Example. For the reaction:
$$A \rightarrow B + C$$

$k = 1 \times 10^{-4}$ sec.$^{-1}$ at 25° C. and 2×10^{-4} sec.$^{-1}$ at 35° C.

(a) Calculate ΔH_a in the temperature range.
(b) Calculate k at 40° C.

    a. $\log \dfrac{2 \times 10^{-4}}{1 \times 10^{-4}} = \dfrac{\Delta H_a(10)}{(2.30)(1.99)(308)(298)}.$

         $\Delta H_a = 12,600$ cal./mole.

    b. $\log \dfrac{k}{2 \times 10^{-4}} = \dfrac{(12600)(5)}{(2.30)(1.99)(313)(308)}.$

         $k = 2.78 \times 10^{-4}$ sec.$^{-1}$

The Energy of Activation

In a gas some molecules are moving rapidly and some are moving very slowly. At a given temperature, the distribution of velocities is given by the *Maxwell distribution law*. This is illustrated in Fig. 36, in which $T_2 > T_1$ and c equals the velocity of the molecules.

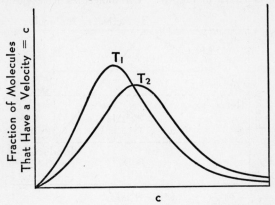

Fig. 36.

The peak of the curve represents the most probable velocity, but it is evident that there are a few molecules with a very high velocity. An increase in temperature raises not only the most probable velocity but also the fraction of molecules having a very high velocity.

Consider a first-order and unimolecular reaction such as the decomposition of gaseous N_2O_5 into N_2O_4 and O_2. Only molecules of N_2O_5 which have a kinetic energy equal to the energy of activation can react. For N_2O_5, ΔH_a equals 24,700 cal./mole. This is equivalent to a velocity of 1.38×10^5 cm./sec., since:

$$E = \tfrac{1}{2}Mc^2,$$

in which: E = energy in ergs,

M = molecular weight,

c = velocity in centimeters/second.

$$(24700)(4.18)(10^7) = \tfrac{1}{2}(108)c^2.$$

$$c = 1.38 \times 10^5 \text{ cm./sec.}$$

Thus, N_2O_5 molecules having velocities of 1.38×10^5 cm./sec. or more are capable of undergoing chemical reaction. Such molecules are said to be *activated molecules*. The number of activated molecules is commonly doubled (or even trebled) if the temperature is raised 10°.

The mechanism by which reactants are converted into products can be represented as follows:

$$\text{Reactants} \overset{\text{slow}}{\rightleftharpoons} \text{Activated Molecules} \overset{\text{fast}}{\rightarrow} \text{Products.}$$

The relationship between the heat of reaction, ΔH, and the energy of activation is shown in Fig. 37. The molecules of reactants need to

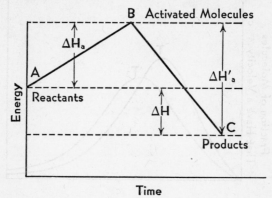

Fig. 37.

absorb a certain amount of energy, ΔH_a, so that they become activated molecules. The activated molecules can then react to form the products and in so doing evolve an amount of energy equal to $\Delta H_a'$. At constant pressure, the heat of reaction, ΔH, is:

$$\Delta H = \Delta H_a - \Delta H_a'.$$

Since the step from activated molecules to products evolves more energy than that absorbed in the step from reactants to activated molecules, the reaction described is exothermic.

Theories of Reaction Rates

According to the collision theory of reaction rates for a bimolecular reaction, two molecules in order to react must (1) collide and (2) be activated molecules. From these assumptions it can be shown that:

$$k = s e^{-\frac{\Delta H_a}{RT}},$$

in which: s = number of molecules colliding per ml. per sec. in a reaction system containing 1 mole of each reactant per liter,

$e^{-\frac{\Delta H_a}{RT}}$ = fraction of the molecules which are activated.

The significance of the terms in the empirical equation can now be seen. The collision theory works well only when applied to relatively simple molecules.

A more comprehensive theory — the theory of absolute reaction rates — has been developed on the basis of statistical mechanics and is applicable to any reaction. The assumption is made that, before reacting, molecules form an "activated complex" which is in equilibrium with the reactants. The sequence can be represented as follows:

$$A + B \rightleftarrows [AB^*] \overset{k}{\rightarrow} \text{Products.}$$
$$\underset{\text{Reactants}}{} \quad \underset{\substack{\text{Activated} \\ \text{Complex}}}{}$$

The rate is thus seen to be controlled by the concentration of the activated complex, and it can be shown that:

$$k = \frac{RT}{Nh} e^{-\frac{\Delta F_a}{RT}},$$

in which: k = rate constant,
  R = gas constant in ergs/deg.-mole,
  T = absolute temperature,
  N = Avogadro's number,
  h = Planck's constant = 6.62×10^{-27} erg-secs.,
  e = 2.718 = base of natural logarithms,
  ΔF_a = free energy of activation.

Catalysis

A *catalyst* is a substance which alters the rate of a chemical reaction but is itself unchanged at the end of the reaction. *Catalysis* is the alteration of the rate of a reaction. A catalyst which slows down a reaction is called a *negative catalyst*. If the catalyst and the reaction mixture form a single phase, the process is called *homogeneous catalysis*. If the catalyst forms a separate phase, the process is called *heterogeneous catalysis*.

Criteria of Catalysis.   Certain characteristics are found in all catalytic processes:

(1) The catalyst remains chemically unchanged at the end of the reaction. However, a change in physical form may take place. For example, smooth platinum which is used as a catalyst in the oxidation of ammonia becomes roughened. This indicates that the catalyst probably takes part in the chemical reaction with regeneration at a later stage.

(2) The catalyst cannot affect the equilibrium constant in a reversible reaction. A catalyst simply hastens the rate of attainment of equilibrium. Thus, a catalyst must accelerate the rate of the reverse reaction to the same extent that it accelerates the rate of the forward reaction.

(3) The catalyst does not initiate a reaction. It merely accelerates a reaction already occurring however slowly. A catalyst probably functions by providing a path for the catalyzed reaction which has a lower energy of activation than the path of the uncatalyzed reaction.

Homogeneous Catalysis. An example of homogeneous catalysis in the gas phase is the oxidation of sulfur dioxide using nitrogen dioxide as a catalyst. The simplified reactions are:

$$\text{First step: } NO_2 + SO_2 \rightarrow SO_3 + NO.$$
$$\text{Second step: } NO + \tfrac{1}{2} O_2 \rightarrow NO_2.$$
$$\text{Net reaction: } SO_2 + \tfrac{1}{2} O_2 \rightarrow SO_3.$$

Note that the reaction proceeds in a stepwise manner. The catalyst enters into the reaction and forms an intermediate compound in the first step. The catalyst is then regenerated in the second step. Such intermediate compound formation is typical of homogeneous catalysis.

Heterogeneous Catalysis. An important type of heterogeneous catalysis involves a gas-phase reaction catalyzed by a solid. For example, finely divided platinum catalyzes the union of hydrogen and oxygen to form water. The reaction in such cases undoubtedly takes place on the surface of the catalyst, and thus the condition of this surface has a profound effect on the catalytic activity.

Poisons and Promoters. Foreign substances which tend to decrease greatly the activity of a catalyst are called *poisons*. For example, a minute amount of arsenic can poison a platinum catalyst by forming a surface compound of platinum arsenide.

Cases are known in which a small amount of substance will increase greatly the activity of a given catalyst although the substance itself has little or no catalytic activity. Such a substance is called a *promoter*.

Review Questions and Problems

1. Derive:

(a) $k = \dfrac{2.303}{t} \log \dfrac{c_0}{c}$.

(b) $t_{\frac{1}{2}} = \dfrac{0.693}{k}$.

(c) $k = \dfrac{1}{t} \dfrac{x}{a(a-x)}$.

(d) $t_{\frac{1}{2}} = \dfrac{1}{ka}$.

(e) $\log \dfrac{k_2}{k_1} = \dfrac{\Delta H_a (T_2 - T_1)}{2.303\, RT_2 T_1}$.

2. Define:

(a) first-order reaction; (b) unimolecular reaction; (c) second-order reaction; (d) bimolecular reaction; (e) zero-order reaction; (f) catalysis; (g) heterogeneous catalysis; (h) homogeneous catalysis; (i) poison; (j) promoter.

3. State the characteristic units of the rate constants for (a) a first-order reaction; (b) a second-order reaction.

4. Summarize the method by which the order of a reaction can be determined by a graphical procedure.

5. How may ΔH_a be determined graphically?

6. In terms of the collision theory, what is the significance of s in the Arrhenius equation when applied to a bimolecular gas reaction?

7. For the reaction, $A \rightarrow$ Products, the following data were obtained at 25° C. in which c_A represents the concentration of A in mole/l. present at time t:

t (sec.)	0	5	10	20	30
c_A	0.461	0.371	0.298	0.196	0.123

Show by substitution into formula and by graphing that the reaction is first order. Calculate $t_{\frac{1}{2}}$.

8. For a certain first-order reaction, $t_{\frac{1}{2}}$ equals 100 sec. How long will it take for the reaction to be 90% completed?

9. A certain substance, A, is mixed with an equimolar amount of B. At the end of 100 sec. one-half of the original amount of A has reacted. How much of A will have reacted in 200 sec. if the reaction with respect to A is (a) zero order; (b) first order; (c) second order?

10. For the reaction: $A + B \rightarrow C + D$, $k = 1 \times 10^{-5}$ liter/mole-min. at 20° C. and $k = 3 \times 10^{-5}$ liter/mole-min. at 30° C. Calculate ΔH_a and k at 40° C.

11

Electrolytic Conductance

Electrochemistry concerns the conversion of electrical energy into chemical energy and vice versa. The reader should review material from elementary electrochemistry before studying this section.

Fundamental Relationships

The fundamental relationships among certain electrical units are stated by means of equations.

Ohm's Law. Ohm's law states that:

$$I = \frac{E}{R}, \qquad\qquad \textbf{11:1}$$

in which: $\quad I$ = current in amperes,

E = electromotive force in volts,

R = resistance in ohms.

The Coulomb. Coulombs = amperes × seconds.

Joule's Law. Electrical energy in joules = volts × coulombs.

Electrical Conduction

Metals and solutions of electrolytes have the property of readily conducting an electric current.

Metallic Conduction. Metallic conduction: (1) consists of the flow of electrons in the conductor; (2) involves no change in the chemical properties of the conductor; (3) involves no transfer of ponderable matter; and (4) generally shows an increase in resistance as the temperature is increased.

Electrolytic Conduction. Electrolytic conduction: (1) consists of the movement of ions in solution; (2) involves chemical reactions which take place at electrodes; (3) involves the transfer of ponderable matter; and (4) generally shows a decrease in resistance as the temperature is increased because the viscosity of the medium and the

112

degree of hydration of the ions decrease with increasing temperature.

The discussion in this chapter is concerned with electrolytic conduction.

Electrolysis

If two electrodes are placed in a solution of an electrolyte and an electric current is passed through the solution, positive ions (cations) are attracted to the negative electrode (the cathode) and negative ions (anions) are attracted to the positive electrode (the anode). Such an arrangement is called a *cell*. At the cathode, cations pick up excess electrons and are thereby reduced. The anions lose electrons at the anode and are thereby oxidized.

For example, if a solution of $CuCl_2$ is electrolyzed with inert electrodes, the following reactions take place:

$$\text{at the cathode: } Cu^{++} + 2\epsilon \rightarrow Cu \text{ (Reduction)},$$
$$\text{at the anode: } 2\,Cl^- \rightarrow Cl_2 + 2\epsilon \text{ (Oxidation)},$$

in which the electron is represented by ϵ. The number of electrons produced at one electrode is equal to the number of electrons consumed at the other electrode. Chemical decomposition by means of an electric current in the manner just described is called *electrolysis*.

The Mechanism of Electrolysis. Usually there are several different kinds of ions around the electrodes since water slightly ionizes to give some hydrogen and hydroxyl ions:

$$H_2O \rightleftarrows H^+ + OH^-.$$

Thus if a solution of $NaNO_3$ is electrolyzed the following reactions take place:

$$\text{at the cathode: } H^+ + \epsilon \rightarrow \tfrac{1}{2} H_2,$$
$$\text{at the anode: } OH^- \rightarrow \tfrac{1}{4} O_2 + \tfrac{1}{2} H_2O + \epsilon.$$

If silver electrodes are used in the electrolysis of a solution of $AgNO_3$, the silver anode simply goes into solution while silver is being deposited at the cathode:

$$\text{cathode: } Ag^+ + \epsilon \rightarrow Ag,$$
$$\text{anode: } Ag \rightarrow Ag^+ + \epsilon.$$

However, in all cases (1) reduction or gain of electrons takes place at the cathode and (2) oxidation or loss of electrons takes place at the anode.

Faraday's Laws of Electrolysis. According to Faraday's laws:

1. The mass of any substance deposited or dissolved at an electrode

the compartment under consideration (if the solute migrates into the compartment under consideration, $\epsilon_{migration}$ is added; otherwise it is subtracted in the above equation),

$\epsilon_{electrode}$ = equivalents of solute which the compartment under consideration gains or loses as a result of the reaction at the electrode (if additional ions are produced as a result of electrolysis, $\epsilon_{electrode}$ is added in the above equation).

Thus, the signs of $\epsilon_{migration}$ and $\epsilon_{electrode}$ depend on the compartment under consideration and the nature of the electrode reaction. For Ag^+ in the cathode compartment, $\epsilon_{migration}$ is positive and $\epsilon_{electrode}$ is negative, and vice versa for the anode compartment.

It follows from the definition of the transference numbers that:

$$n_c = \frac{\text{change in equivalents due to migration of cation}}{\text{total equivalents migrating}},$$

$$n_c = \frac{\epsilon_{migration}}{\epsilon_{electrode}},$$

$$n_a = \frac{\text{change in equivalents due to migration of anion}}{\text{total equivalents migrating}},$$

$$n_a = \frac{\epsilon_{migration}}{\epsilon_{electrode}}.$$

The change in equivalents due to migration of cation or anion can be determined from $\epsilon_{migration}$. The sum of the equivalents migrating is equal to the sum of the equivalents of silver deposited in the silver coulometer.

Example. The apparatus in Fig. 38 was filled with a $AgNO_3$ solution containing 0.02178 equivalent of Ag^+ per 1000 grams of H_2O. After a small current was passed for two hours, the solution in the anode compartment was analyzed, and it was found that 0.000696 equivalent of Ag^+ was present in 23.14 grams of water. This solution originally contained

$$\frac{0.02178}{1000}(23.14)$$

or 0.000504 equivalent. During electrolysis, 0.000361 equivalent of silver was deposited in the coulometer. Calculate n_c and n_a.

$$\epsilon_{fin.} = \epsilon_{init.} - \epsilon_{mig.} + \epsilon_{el.}.$$
$$0.000696 = 0.000504 - \epsilon_{mig.} + 0.000361.$$
$$\epsilon_{mig.} = 0.000169.$$
$$n_c = \frac{0.000169}{0.000361} = 0.468.$$
$$n_a = 1 - 0.468 = 0.532.$$

Transference numbers vary slightly with concentration and with temperature. As the temperature rises transference numbers tend to become equal, i.e., they approach a limiting value of 0.5. Hydrogen ions and hydroxyl ions both possess abnormally high transference numbers.

Specific and Equivalent Conductance

The *specific resistance* is the resistance of a column of material one centimeter long and one centimeter square in cross section. The *specific conductance*, L, is the reciprocal of the specific resistance. L is the conductance of a one-centimeter cube of material; it has the units of reciprocal ohms, or *mhos*. The *equivalent conductance* of a solution, Λ, is defined by the following equation:

$$\Lambda = VL, \qquad \textbf{11:3}$$

in which V = volume of solution in ml. which contains one equivalent weight of solute.

But $V = 1000/c$, in which c = normality of solution, or:

$$\Lambda = \frac{1000L}{c}. \qquad \textbf{11:4}$$

Thus Λ has the units of mhos per equivalent.

Determination of Conductance. The specific conductance, L, could theoretically be determined by measuring the resistance of a cell in which one centimeter cube of solution is enclosed between two platinized platinum electrodes exactly one centimeter on edge and exactly one centimeter apart. Since this is not feasible, in practice a glass vessel containing two electrodes of any convenient size and distance apart is used. This is a *conductance cell*.

It is then necessary to determine experimentally a factor called the *cell constant*, k. This is done by filling the conductance cell with a solution for which L is known and measuring the resistance, R, of the cell. Then:

$$L = \frac{k}{R} \qquad \textbf{11:5}$$

or:
$$k = LR. \qquad \textbf{11:6}$$

Once k is known for a particular cell, the cell can then be used to determine L for unknown solutions.

Example. A conductance cell had a resistance of 165 ohms when filled with 0.02-molar KCl at 25° C. For such a solution $L = 0.00277$ mho.

The same cell when filled with 0.01-molar NaCl had a resistance of 384 ohms. Calculate L and Λ.

$$k = LR = (0.00277)(165) = 0.457.$$

$$L = \frac{k}{R} = \frac{0.457}{384} = 0.00119 \text{ mho.}$$

$$\Lambda = \frac{(1000)(0.00119)}{0.01} = 119 \text{ mhos/equivalent.}$$

Thus the measurement of specific conductance and the equivalent conductance of solutions is based on the measurement of resistance. This is usually accomplished by means of a Wheatstone bridge. Alternating current of about a thousand cycles per second is used to prevent complications at the electrodes. Direct current would produce gas bubbles at the electrodes which would greatly affect the resistance of the cell. The electrodes are platinized (i.e., covered with a deposit of finely divided platinum) to further minimize evolution of gases at the electrodes. Exceptionally pure water, called *conductance water*, is used in preparing solutions for conductance measurements.

Equivalent Conductance at Infinite Dilution. If Λ is plotted versus $\sqrt{c}$ (Fig. 39) a straight line is obtained for strong electrolytes (e.g., KCl), but a nonlinear relationship is exhibited by weak electrolytes (e.g., acetic acid). The limiting value of Λ as $c \rightarrow 0$ is called the *equivalent conductance at infinite dilution* and is given the symbol Λ_0. For strong electrolytes, Λ_0 can be obtained by extrapolation as shown in Fig. 39.

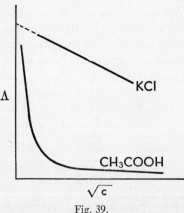

Fig. 39.

KOHLRAUSCH'S LAW. In order to determine Λ_0 for weak electrolytes, the law of Kohlrausch is applied. According to this law, at infinite dilution the ions behave independently of each other, and:

$$\Lambda_0 = l_c + l_a, \qquad\qquad\qquad \textbf{11:7}$$

in which: l_c = equivalent conductance of the cation at infinite dilution,

l_a = equivalent conductance of the anion at infinite dilution.

Example. Calculate Λ_0 for propionic acid, CH_3CH_2COOH (or HPr), given that:

$$\Lambda_0 \text{ for HCl} = 426.0,$$
$$\Lambda_0 \text{ for NaPr} = 85.9,$$
$$\Lambda_0 \text{ for NaCl} = 126.4.$$

These three substances are all strong electrolytes, and Λ_0 for them can be obtained by extrapolation. Then:

$$\begin{aligned}
\Lambda_{0_{HPr}} &= \Lambda_{0_{NaPr}} + \Lambda_{0_{HCl}} - \Lambda_{0_{NaCl}} \\
&= l_{Na^+} + l_{Pr^-} + l_{H^+} + l_{Cl^-} - l_{Na^+} - l_{Cl^-} \\
&= l_{H^+} + l_{Pr^-} \\
&= 85.9 + 426.0 - 126.4 \\
&= 385.5 \text{ mhos/equivalent.}
\end{aligned}$$

Λ_0 FROM TRANSFERENCE NUMBERS. Since the fraction of the total current carried by an ion is equal to its transference number, it follows that the transference number also represents the fraction of the total conductance due to the ion, or:

$$n_c{}^0 = \frac{l_c}{\Lambda_0}, \qquad\qquad\qquad \textbf{11:8}$$

$$n_a{}^0 = \frac{l_a}{\Lambda_0}, \qquad\qquad\qquad \textbf{11:9}$$

$$l_c = n_c{}^0 \Lambda_0, \qquad\qquad\qquad \textbf{11:10}$$

$$l_a = n_a{}^0 \Lambda_0, \qquad\qquad\qquad \textbf{11:11}$$

in which $n_c{}^0$ and $n_a{}^0$ are the transference numbers at infinite dilution as obtained by extrapolation. In Table 9 are listed values of l_c and l_a at 25° C.

Example. Calculate Λ_0 at 25° C. for acetic acid (HAc) from the data in Table 9.

$$\begin{aligned}
\Lambda_{0_{HAc}} &= l_{H^+} + l_{Ae^-} = 349.8 + 40.9 \\
&= 390.7 \text{ mhos/eq.}
\end{aligned}$$

TABLE 9

EQUIVALENT IONIC CONDUCTANCES AT INFINITE DILUTION
(25° C.)

Cations		Anions	
K^+	73.5	Cl^-	76.3
Na^+	50.1	Br^-	78.4
Li^+	38.7	I^-	76.8
NH_4^+	73.4	NO_3^-	71.4
H^+	349.8	OH^-	198.0
Ag^+	61.9	Acetate$^-$	40.9
$\frac{1}{2} Ca^{++}$	59.5	Propionate$^-$	35.8
$\frac{1}{2} Ba^{++}$	63.6	$\frac{1}{2} SO_4^{--}$	79.8

Conductometric Titration

If a strong acid (e.g., HCl) is titrated with a strong base (e.g., NaOH), the conductance gradually decreases, passes through a minimum at the end point, and then increases again. This is because as the neutralization proceeds the fast-moving hydrogen ions are replaced by the slower-moving sodium ions and hence the conductance decreases. After the end point is reached, however, the excess hydroxyl ions (from the NaOH) cause an increase in conductance because of their relatively high speed.

If the strong base used is much more concentrated than the acid, the lines are as shown in I of Fig. 40. The end point corresponds to the intersection of the lines.

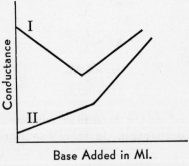

Fig. 40.

If a weak acid (e.g., acetic acid) is titrated with a strong base, the conductance changes are as shown in II of Fig. 40. This is due to the low conductance of the acetic acid solution. The addition of some

NaOH causes some sodium acetate to form. This, being a salt, is a good conductor, and the conductivity of the solution increases. The conductivity continues to increase for this reason until the end point is reached. After this, the addition of excess fast-moving hydroxyl ions causes the conductance to increase even more rapidly. Again, the end point corresponds to the intersection of the two straight lines.

Conductometric titrations are especially useful in the case of colored or turbid solutions where the usual indicators cannot be used.

Decomposition Potential

If two inert electrodes are placed in a solution of an electrolyte and the voltage is gradually increased, the following curve is obtained when I is plotted versus E. See Fig. 41. It is evident that at low

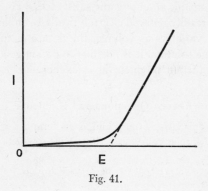

Fig. 41.

voltages practically no current flows. Above a certain voltage a large current starts to flow. This voltage, called the *decomposition voltage*, E_D, is obtained by the extrapolation of the steep line until it cuts the x-axis. The decomposition voltage of $AgNO_3$ is 0.70 volt, of $CuSO_4$ is 1.49 volts, and of $Cd(NO_3)_2$ is 1.98 volts. If a solution containing all these salts is electrolyzed, the silver will be deposited when the external voltage is 0.70 volt. When all the silver has been deposited, the current will fall practically to zero. If the applied voltage is now raised to 1.49 volts, the copper is deposited. After all the copper has been deposited, the cadmium can be plated out by raising the voltage to 1.98 volts.

If a 2-molar solution of HCl is electrolyzed using Pt electrodes, H_2 is obtained at the cathode and Cl_2 at the anode. If a 0.02-molar solution of HCl is electrolyzed, H_2 is obtained at the cathode and O_2

at the anode, because less energy is required to discharge the OH^-, as follows:

$$OH^- \rightarrow \tfrac{1}{4} O_2 + \tfrac{1}{2} H_2O + \epsilon,$$

than is required to discharge Cl^-. At intermediate concentrations a mixture of Cl_2 and O_2 is obtained at the anode. Thus, the products of electrolysis may depend not only on applied voltage, but also on concentration.

If the products of electrolysis accumulate at the electrodes, a cell is set up which produces a countervoltage. The production of such a voltage is called *polarization*.

Electrolytic Oxidation and Reduction

Since reduction takes place at the cathode and oxidation takes place at the anode, electrolysis affords a useful technique for the oxidation or reduction of organic and inorganic substances. For example, nitrobenzene can be readily reduced electrolytically to aniline. By suitable control of such variables as voltage, the nature of the cathode, and the acidity of the solution, it is possible to obtain good yields of such intermediate reduction products as azoxybenzene, azobenzene, and hydrazobenzene.

Review Questions and Problems

1. State Faraday's laws in words and in the form of an equation.

2. Define: (a) specific resistance; (b) specific conductance; (c) equivalent conductance.

3. How may conductance titrations be used to determine the end point in neutralization reactions?

4. Sketch the curves obtained when conductance is plotted versus ml. of acid added for the following titrations:

(a) $NaOH + HCl$; (b) $NaOH + CH_3COOH$.

5. A current of 0.100 ampere flows for 100 seconds through a solution of $Pb(NO_3)_2$. How many grams of lead are deposited at the cathode?

6. If Λ_0 for $ClCH_2COONa$ is 89.8 at 25° C., calculate Λ_0 for $ClCH_2COOH$ using data from Table 9.

7. Calculate l_c for $ClCH_2COO^-$ using data given in Problem 6.

8. A solution of $CuSO_4$ was electrolyzed in the apparatus shown in Fig. 38 using copper electrodes. A given weight of H_2O in the anode compartment contained 0.03820 equivalent of Cu^{++} before electrolysis and 0.04504 equivalent of Cu^{++} after. During the electrolysis 0.00950 equivalent of silver was deposited in the silver coulometer. The anode reaction is:

$$Cu \rightarrow Cu^{++} + 2 \epsilon.$$

Calculate n_c and n_a for $CuSO_4$.

12

Electromotive Force

An electrochemical cell is an arrangement of two electrodes and an electrolyte. Such a cell is capable of producing an electric current as a result of a chemical reaction within the cell. If an electric current is passed through the cell, a chemical reaction takes place at the electrodes. A simple example is a modified Daniell cell, which consists of a strip of zinc immersed in a solution of zinc ions and a strip of copper immersed in a solution of cupric ions, the two solutions being connected by a U tube containing a solution of zinc ions. See Fig. 42.

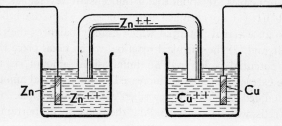

Fig. 42.

The whole cell consists of two half-cells — in this case a zinc half-cell and a copper half-cell. If a wire connects the zinc electrode to the copper electrode, a current flows and the following reactions take place:

$$Zn \rightarrow Zn^{++} + 2\epsilon \text{ (oxidation at left electrode).}$$
$$Cu^{++} + 2\epsilon \rightarrow Cu \text{ (reduction at right electrode).}$$

The cell reaction can be divided into two parts — oxidation (electron loss) and reduction (electron gain). In general, each electrode involves a contact between a metal and a solution of the corresponding metal ions. There exists at the surface between the metal and the solution a difference in potential which is called the *electrode potential*. The potential of the above cell, E_{cell}, is:

123

$$E_{\text{cell}} = E_{\text{left}} + E_{\text{right}} + E_{\text{junction}},$$

in which E_{left} = electrode potential of the left-hand electrode,
              E_{right} = electrode potential of the right-hand electrode,
              E_{junction} = potential which results from the contact between
                           the solution containing the zinc ions and the
                           solution containing the cupric ions.

For practical purposes, the junction potential may be eliminated by filling the U tube with saturated KCl. Such a device is called a *salt bridge*. Then:

$$E_{\text{cell}} = E_{\text{left}} + E_{\text{right}}.$$

The above cell can be represented as follows:

$$\text{Zn;Zn}^{++} \parallel \text{Cu}^{++}\text{;Cu,}$$

in which the semicolon implies contact between two different phases and the sign $\parallel$ indicates that the junction potential has been rendered negligible by means of a salt bridge.

In dealing with the energy interrelationships of cells, thermodynamic principles are applicable if the cells are reversible. A cell is reversible if: (1) no chemical action occurs when the cell is connected to an external potential which exactly balances the potential of the cell, and (2) the chemical reaction, which takes place when the external potential is lowered an infinitesimal amount, is reversed when the external potential is increased an infinitesimal amount.

The modified Daniell cell described above is reversible. Only reversible cells will be considered in the subsequent portion of this chapter.

The Measurement of Electromotive Force

The electromotive force or potential of a cell cannot be measured accurately by connecting the cell to a voltmeter because the voltmeter draws an appreciable current from the cell. This changes the concentration of the electrolyte around the electrodes, which in turn causes a change in the potential of the cell. In addition, if an appreciable current flows, part of the potential is used to overcome the internal resistance of the cell, so that the voltmeter reading will not represent the true potential of the cell.

Determination of Electromotive Force. Accurate determination of the potential of a cell must be made under conditions where practically no current flows. This is done conveniently by means of a potentiometer. See the diagram shown in Fig. 43, in which:

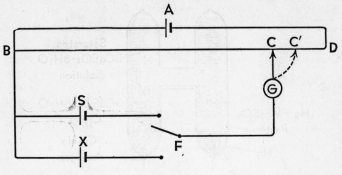

Fig. 43.

BD = uniform conductor of fairly high resistance,
A = "working cell" of constant voltage as a dry cell,
X = cell whose potential is to be determined,
S = "standard cell," a cell whose potential is known,
C = movable contact,
G = galvanometer,
F = switch.

The cell S is connected to B by the switch F, and the movable contact C is moved along BD until no current flows through the galvanometer G. The movable contact now rests at C. The length BC is noted. By means of the switch F, cell X is connected to B and the procedure is repeated. The movable contact now rests at C' and the length BC' is noted. Then:

$$\frac{E_x}{E_s} = \frac{\text{Fall of potential between } B \text{ and } C'}{\text{Fall of potential between } B \text{ and } C}$$
$$= \frac{\text{Resistance of } BC'}{\text{Resistance of } BC},$$

or since resistance is proportional to length:

$$\frac{E_x}{E_s} = \frac{\text{Length } BC'}{\text{Length } BC},$$

in which: E_x = potential of cell X,
E_s = potential of standard cell S.

The Weston Standard Cell. The most commonly used standard cell is the Weston standard cell shown in Fig. 44 (p. 126). The left-hand arm of the H-shaped glass cell contains a paste of Hg and Hg_2SO_4

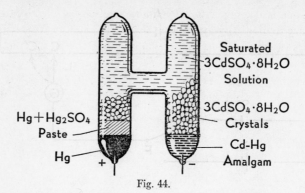

Fig. 44.

which floats on a layer of pure Hg. The right-hand arm contains a Cd-Hg amalgam which contains 10–13% Cd by weight. The cell is filled with a saturated solution of $3CdSO_4 \cdot 8H_2O$ containing an excess of solid $3CdSO_4 \cdot 8H_2O$. Connection to the cell is made by means of platinum wires sealed through the bottom of each arm.

The voltage of this cell is constant at a given temperature unless an abnormally large current is drawn. The voltage of the cell is 1.01830 international volts at 20.0° C. and decreases 4×10^{-5} volt for every degree rise in temperature. When the cell is used as a source of current the following reaction takes place:

$$3 \, Cd_{(s)} + 3 \, Hg_2SO_{4(s)} + 8 \, H_2O_{(l)} \rightarrow 3CdSO_4 \cdot 8H_2O_{(s)} + 6 \, Hg_{(l)}.$$

Activities of Electrolytes and Ions

Before proceeding, it is convenient to introduce the concept of activity. Activities may be thought of as effective concentrations. Molalities may be converted into activities by the following equation:

$$a = m\gamma,$$

in which: a = activity,
m = molality,
γ = activity coefficient.

Equation 8:6 is not thermodynamically exact because of the nonideal behavior of real solutions. If activities are substituted for concentrations in equation 8:6, a true equilibrium constant is obtained.

For dilute solutions of nonelectrolytes, the difference between activities and concentrations can be considered negligible. This is not true for solutions of electrolytes because the forces of interionic attraction cause large deviations from ideal behavior. Therefore, unless one is dealing with very dilute solutions of electrolytes it is necessary to use activities in place of concentrations. As the solution becomes extremely dilute, activity and concentration become identical (i.e., $\gamma \to 1$).

A *uni-univalent electrolyte* is one which contains a cation whose valence is $+1$ and an anion whose valence is -1. For such an electrolyte:

$$a_{el} = (a_+)(a_-),$$

in which: $a_{el} =$ activity of the electrolyte,

$a_+ =$ activity of cation,

$a_- =$ activity of anion.

The mean activity coefficient, γ, of a uni-univalent electrolyte is by definition:

$$\gamma = \sqrt{(\gamma_+)(\gamma_-)}.$$

Then: $a_{el} = (m\gamma_+)(m\gamma_-) = m^2\gamma^2.$

In dilute solutions it may be assumed that:

$$a_+ = a_- = m\gamma.$$

The mean activity, $a_\pm$, of a uni-univalent electrolyte is defined as:

$$a_\pm = \sqrt{a_{el}}$$

or: $a_\pm = m\gamma.$

This treatment can be extended to other than uni-univalent electrolytes.

The activities of pure solids and pure liquids are equal to one.

Reference Electrodes

Since the electromotive force (EMF) or potential of a cell equals the sum of the potentials of the two half-cells and since cell potentials can be determined as explained above, it is evident that the potential of one half-cell can be determined if the potential of the whole cell and the potential of the other half-cell are known. For this purpose reference electrodes (half-cells of known potentials) are used.

The Hydrogen Electrode. A common reference electrode is the standard hydrogen electrode. It consists of a platinized platinum electrode dipping into a solution of hydrogen ions whose activity equals 1.000 while hydrogen gas bubbles over the electrode at a pressure of 1 atmosphere. The potential of this electrode is arbitrarily chosen as 0.000 volt, and all other reference electrodes and half-cells are compared to it.

The Calomel Electrode. One of the most convenient reference electrodes is the calomel electrode. It consists of a drop of mercury in contact with a solution of KCl which is saturated with respect to Hg_2Cl_2 (calomel). Three different concentrations of KCl are commonly used, 0.1 N, 1 N, and saturated. Each of these three reference electrodes has a characteristic voltage at 25° C., and these voltages are listed in Table 11.

Relation between Free Energy and Electric Energy

If a cell operates reversibly at constant temperature and pressure, the electrical work done by the system per mole of reactant consumed is nFE, in which n is the valence change, F is the faraday or 96,500 coulombs, and E is the electromotive force of the cell. At the same time the free energy of the system decreases by the amount ΔF. Thus:

$$-\Delta F = nFE$$

or:

$$\Delta F = -nFE. \qquad \textbf{12:1}$$

This important equation represents the link between thermodynamics and electrochemistry. By means of this equation it is possible to determine thermodynamic quantities from electromotive-force measurements.

Example. The following cell:

$$Zn;Zn^{++} \parallel Cu^{++};Cu$$

has a potential of 1.00 volt. Calculate ΔF for the reaction in which one mole of zinc is consumed.

$$\Delta F = -nFE$$
$$= -(2)(96500)(1.00)$$
$$= -193,000 \text{ joules.}$$
$$\frac{-193000}{4.18} = -46,200 \text{ calories.}$$

According to the Gibbs-Helmholtz equation:

$$\Delta F = \Delta H + T\left(\frac{d\Delta F}{dT}\right)_p.$$

Substituting $-nFE$ for ΔF:

$$-nFE = \Delta H - nFT\left(\frac{dE}{dT}\right)_p. \qquad \textbf{12:2}$$

This equation gives the heat of the chemical reaction occurring within the cell as a function of the electromotive force and the temperature coefficient of the cell. Since electromotive-force measurements are usually more precise than thermal measurements, heats of reaction determined by equation 12:2 are often more accurate than the same quantities determined from calorimetric measurements.

Classification of Cells

Table 10 shows several different types of reversible cells (commonly referred to simply as electrodes).

TABLE 10
TYPES OF HALF-CELLS OR ELECTRODES

		Example
1.	Metal;metal ion	$Zn;Zn^{++}$
2.	Amalgam electrode;ion	$(Cd + Hg);Cd^{++}$
3.	Inert electrode;ions of different valence	$Pt;Sn^{+2},Sn^{+4}$
4.	Inert electrode;nonmetal;ion	$Pt;I_{2_{(s)}};I^-$
5.	Inert electrode;gas;ion	$Pt;H_2;H^+$
6.	Electrode;insoluble salt;ion	$Ag;AgBr_{(s)};Br^-$

In the example column in Table 10, a semicolon signifies contact between two different phases, and the comma signifies different ions present in the same solution.

Any two half-cells may be combined to form a whole cell whose electromotive force is the algebraic sum of the potentials of the two half-cells.

Electrochemical Conventions

The significance of the signs of electrode potentials and cells, and the information gained from them, may be better understood by use of the following conventions:

1. Since $\Delta F = -nFE$, it is clear that if E is positive then ΔF will be negative and the corresponding chemical reaction will be spontaneous.

2. All cells are arbitrarily written so that oxidation takes place in the left-hand half-cell and reduction in the right-hand half-cell. The cell reaction is the sum of the two half-cell reactions.

Example. Write the half-cell reactions and the whole-cell reaction for the following cells:

(a) $$A;A^+ \parallel B^+;B.$$

oxidation at the left: $A \rightarrow A^+ + \epsilon.$
reduction at the right: $B^+ + \epsilon \rightarrow B.$
cell reaction: $A + B^+ \rightarrow A^+ + B.$

(b) $$A;A^+ \parallel X^-;X.$$

$$A \rightarrow A^+ + \epsilon$$
$$\underline{X + \epsilon \rightarrow X^-}$$
$$A + X \rightarrow A^+ + X^-$$

3. The standard electrode potential, E^0, is defined as the potential of a half-cell in which all the ions involved are at unit activity (i.e., $a = 1$). The standard electrode potentials of several electrodes at 25° C. are given in Table 11. They are listed as oxidation potentials, i.e., the half-cell reactions corresponding to them are oxidation reactions. If the electrode is used as a left-hand half-cell, the E^0 values are used just as they are found in Table 11. However, if the electrodes are used as right-hand half-cells, the *sign* of the value must be changed.

TABLE 11

STANDARD ELECTRODE POTENTIALS AT 25° C.

Electrode	Reaction	E^0 (volts)
K;K$^+$	K → K$^+$ + ϵ	+2.924
Na;Na$^+$	Na → Na$^+$ + ϵ	+2.714
Zn;Zn^{++}	Zn → Zn^{++} + 2 ϵ	+0.761
Fe;Fe^{++}	Fe → Fe^{++} + 2 ϵ	+0.441
Cd;Cd^{++}	Cd → Cd^{++} + 2 ϵ	+0.402
Co;Co^{++}	Co → Co^{++} + 2 ϵ	+0.283
Ni;Ni^{++}	Ni → Ni^{++} + 2 ϵ	+0.236
Sn;Sn^{++}	Sn → Sn^{++} + 2 ϵ	+0.140
Pb;Pb^{++}	Pb → Pb^{++} + 2 ϵ	+0.126
Pt;H$_2$;H$^+$	$\frac{1}{2}$ H$_2$ → H$^+$ + ϵ	±0.000
Pt;Ti^{+3},Ti^{+4}	Ti^{+3} → Ti^{+4} + ϵ	−0.040
Ag;AgBr$_{(s)}$;Br$^-$	Ag + Br$^-$ → AgBr + ϵ	−0.073
Pt;Sn^{++},Sn^{+4}	Sn^{++} → Sn^{+4} + 2 ϵ	−0.150
Pt;Cu$^+$,Cu^{++}	Cu$^+$ → Cu^{++} + ϵ	−0.167
Ag;AgCl$_{(s)}$,Cl$^-$	Ag + Cl$^-$ → AgCl + ϵ	−0.222
Saturated calomel electrode	Hg + Cl$^-$ → $\frac{1}{2}$ Hg$_2$Cl$_2$ + ϵ	−0.242
Normal calomel electrode	Hg + Cl$^-$ → $\frac{1}{2}$ Hg$_2$Cl$_2$ + ϵ	−0.280
0.1-N calomel electrode	Hg + Cl$^-$ → $\frac{1}{2}$ Hg$_2$Cl$_2$ + ϵ	−0.334
Cu;Cu^{++}	Cu → Cu^{++} + 2 ϵ	−0.340
Pt;Fe(CN)$_6^{-4}$,Fe(CN)$_6^{-3}$	Fe(CN)$_6^{-4}$ → Fe(CN)$_6^{-3}$ + ϵ	−0.356
Pt;I$_{2(s)}$;I$^-$	I$^-$ → $\frac{1}{2}$ I$_2$ + ϵ	−0.536
Pt;Fe^{++},Fe^{+3}	Fe^{++} → Fe^{+3} + ϵ	−0.771
Ag;Ag$^+$	Ag → Ag$^+$ + ϵ	−0.799
Hg;Hg$_2^{++}$	Hg → $\frac{1}{2}$ Hg$_2^{++}$ + ϵ	−0.799
Pt;Hg$_2^{++}$,Hg^{++}	Hg$_2^{++}$ → 2 Hg^{++} + 2 ϵ	−0.906
Pt;Br$_{2(l)}$;Br$^-$	Br$^-$ → $\frac{1}{2}$ Br$_2$ + ϵ	−1.066
Pt;Cl$_{2(g)}$;Cl$^-$	Cl$^-$ → $\frac{1}{2}$ Cl$_2$ + ϵ	−1.358
Pt;Ce^{+3},Ce^{+4}	Ce^{+3} → Ce^{+4} + ϵ	−1.610

Example. Give the cell reaction and calculate the electromotive force for the following cell at 25° C.

$$Ag; Ag^+_{(a=1)} \parallel Cu^{++}_{(a=1)}; Cu.$$

Is the reaction spontaneous?

The cell reaction is:

$$
\begin{array}{r}
2\,Ag \rightarrow 2\,Ag^+ + 2\,\epsilon \\
Cu^{++} + 2\,\epsilon \rightarrow Cu \\
\hline
2\,Ag + Cu^{++} \rightarrow 2\,Ag^+ + Cu
\end{array}
$$

$$
\begin{aligned}
E^0 &= E^0_{\text{left}} + E^0_{\text{right}} \\
&= (-0.799) + (+0.340) = -0.459 \text{ volt.}
\end{aligned}
$$

Note. Since the copper half-cell appears at the right, the sign of the value in Table 11 must be changed.

Since E^0 is negative, the reaction is not spontaneous.

Example. Write the cell which corresponds to the following cell reaction at 25° C.

$$Cu_{(s)} + I_{2(s)} \rightarrow Cu^{++}_{(a=1)} + 2\,I^-_{(a=1)}.$$

Is the reaction spontaneous?

$$Cu; Cu^{++}_{(a=1)} \parallel I^-_{(a=1)}; I_{2(s)}; Pt.$$

$$E^0 = (-0.340) + (+0.536) = +0.196 \text{ volt.}$$

Spontaneous.

4. If the cell reaction is spontaneous, the left electrode is negative (and the right electrode is positive). This is because of the excess of electrons at the left electrode which are produced by the oxidation reaction.

Electromotive Force and Chemical Equilibria

If activities are substituted for concentrations in equation 8:12, it becomes:

$$\Delta F = -RT \ln \frac{a_G{}^g a_H{}^h}{a_A{}^a a_B{}^b} + RT \ln \frac{\bar{a}_G{}^g \bar{a}_H{}^h}{\bar{a}_A{}^a \bar{a}_B{}^b}$$

or:

$$\Delta F = -RT \ln K + RT \ln Q.$$

Since:

$$\Delta F = -nFE:$$

$$E = \frac{RT}{nF} \ln K - \frac{RT}{nF} \ln Q. \qquad 12:3$$

Since:

$$\Delta F^0 = -nFE^0:$$

$$\Delta F^0 = -RT \ln K.$$

$$E^0 = \frac{RT}{nF} \ln K. \qquad 12:4$$

Then substituting equation 12:4 into equation 12:3:

$$E = E^0 - \frac{RT}{nF} \ln Q.$$

This is commonly referred to as the *Nernst equation*. At 25° C.:

$$E = E^0 - \frac{(8.314)(298)(2.303)}{(n)(96500)} \log Q$$

$$= E^0 - \frac{0.0591}{n} \log Q. \qquad \textbf{12:5}$$

This equation gives the electromotive force of a cell as a function of the initial and final activities.

Example. Calculate the equilibrium constant for the following reaction at 25° C.

$$\text{Ni} + \text{Sn}^{++}{}_{(a=1)} \rightarrow \text{Sn} + \text{Ni}^{++}{}_{(a=1)}.$$

$$\text{Ni} \rightarrow \text{Ni}^{++} + 2\ \epsilon.$$

$$\text{Sn}^{++} + 2\ \epsilon \rightarrow \text{Sn}.$$

$$\text{Ni}; \text{Ni}^{++}{}_{(a=1)} \parallel \text{Sn}^{++}{}_{(a=1)}; \text{Sn}.$$

$$E^0{}_{\text{cell}} = (+0.236) + (-0.140) = +0.096 \text{ volt}.$$

$$E^0 = \frac{RT}{nF} \ln K.$$

$$0.096 = \frac{0.0591}{2} \log K.$$

$$\log K = 3.25.$$

$$K = 1780.$$

Example. Calculate the potential of the following cell at 25° C.

$$\text{Ni}; \text{Ni}^{++}{}_{(a=0.4)} \parallel \text{Sn}^{++}{}_{(a=0.3)}; \text{Sn}.$$

$$\text{Ni} + \text{Sn}^{++} \rightarrow \text{Ni}^{++} + \text{Sn}.$$

$$E = E^0 - \frac{0.0591}{n} \log Q$$

$$= 0.096 - \frac{0.0591}{2} \log \frac{0.4}{0.3}$$

$$= 0.092 \text{ volt}.$$

Concentration Cells

If two electrodes of the same material are immersed in solutions of their ions at the same activities, the potential of the cell will be zero. If the activities of the two solutions are different, however, there will be a definite electromotive force produced. Such a cell is called a *concentration cell* and can be illustrated by the following arrangement:

$$\text{M}; \text{M}^+{}_{(a_1)} \parallel \text{M}^+{}_{(a_2)}; \text{M},$$

in which a_1 and a_2 are the activities of M^+ on the left-hand and right-hand side of the cell, respectively. The reactions involved are:

$$M \rightarrow M^+_{(a_1)} + \epsilon$$
$$M^+_{(a_2)} + \epsilon \rightarrow M$$
$$\overline{M^+_{(a_2)} \rightarrow M^+_{(a_1)}}$$

and:
$$E = E^0 - 0.0591 \log \frac{a_1}{a_2}.$$

It is clear that the E^0 values for the two half-cells must be equal in magnitude but opposite in sign; thus E^0 for the whole cell must be zero. Then:

$$E = -0.0591 \log \frac{a_1}{a_2}.$$

Measurement of pH

The pH of a solution is defined by the equation:

$$\text{pH} = -\log a_{H^+} = \log \frac{1}{a_{H^+}}.$$

It can be measured from the potential of the following cell:

$$\text{Pt};H_{2(p=1)};H^+_{(a)} \parallel H^+_{(a=1)};H_{2(p=1)};\text{Pt},$$

in which a = activity of H^+ of the left-hand half-cell. Then:

$$\tfrac{1}{2} H_2 \rightarrow H_a^+ + \epsilon$$
$$\epsilon + H^+_{(a=1)} \rightarrow \tfrac{1}{2} H_2$$
$$\overline{H^+_{(a=1)} \rightarrow H_a^+}$$

and since the above cell is a concentration cell:

$$E = -\frac{0.0591}{1} \log a.$$

$$\text{pH} = -\log a = \frac{E}{0.0591}.$$

In practice it is convenient to substitute a normal calomel electrode for the right-hand half-cell. Then:

$$E = -0.0591 \log a + 0.280$$

and:
$$\text{pH} = -\log a = \frac{E - 0.280}{0.0591}.$$

A very convenient device for measuring the pH of solutions is the glass electrode. If two solutions of different pH are separated by a

glass membrane, the potential established across the membrane is a
function of the pH of the solutions. The cell may be represented as
follows:

Reference electrode	Solution of known pH	Glass membrane	Solution of unknown pH	Reference electrode.

The resistance of such a cell (called a *glass electrode*) is very high.
However, the potential can be measured by means of an electron-tube
voltmeter, and the pH of the unknown solution can then be calculated
from the potential. Portable, rugged instruments are available which
are usually calibrated to read pH directly.

Cells without Transference

The cells considered so far in this chapter are cells involving liquid
junctions. These are called cells with transference. Although it is
possible to reduce the junction potential a great deal by means of a
salt bridge, such cells are not thermodynamically exact.

Cells without transference (i.e., without liquid junctions) are thermodynamically exact. An example is the following cell (in which
m = molality):

$$Ag;AgCl_s;\underset{m_1}{LiCl};(Li\ \&\ Hg);\underset{m_2}{LiCl};AgCl_s;Ag.$$

Such a cell contains no liquid-liquid junction, is reversible to both
cation and anion, and can be used to determine the mean activity of
the electrolyte. Since the cell is a concentration cell, $E^0 = 0$ and:

$$
\begin{aligned}
E &= -\frac{0.0591}{1}\log\frac{a_1}{a_2} \\
  &= -\frac{0.0591}{1}\log\frac{[(a_+)(a_-)]_1}{[(a_+)(a_-)]_2} \\
  &= -\frac{0.0591}{1}\log\frac{(m\gamma)_1^2}{(m\gamma)_2^2} \\
  &= -0.1182\log\frac{m_1\gamma_1}{m_2\gamma_2}.
\end{aligned}
$$

If m_2 is very small, $\gamma_2 = 1$ and γ_1 can be calculated from E. In
practice, γ_1 is best evaluated by an appropriate graphical technique.
Thus it is possible to determine activity coefficients (and hence activities) from electromotive-force measurements.

Formula for the Mercurous Ion

An interesting application of electrode potentials is the determination of the correct formula for the mercurous ion. It can be shown to be Hg_2^{++}.

The oxidation potential of a metal;metal ion electrode is given by:

$$E_1 = E^0 - \frac{0.0591}{n} \log a,$$

in which a = activity of the metal ion. If the solution of metal ions is now diluted to 0.1 of its original value, the potential becomes:

$$E_2 = E^0 - \frac{0.0591}{n} \log 0.1a.$$

The difference in potential is:

$$E_2 - E_1 = -\frac{0.0591}{n} \log \frac{0.1a}{a} = \frac{0.0591}{n}.$$

Thus, at 25° C., a tenfold decrease in metal ion activity causes an increase of $0.0591/n$ volt in the oxidation potential.

However, a tenfold decrease in the concentration of mercurous ion causes an increase of 0.0296 volt in the oxidation potential of the mercury;mercurous ion electrode. Then:

$$0.0296 = \frac{0.0591}{n}$$

or $n = 2$, and the correct formula for the mercurous ion is Hg_2^{++} rather than Hg^+.

Potentiometric Titration

During the titration of a monobasic acid (e.g., HCl) by a base, a sharp change in potential or pH is obtained at the end point. A typical plot of E (or pH) versus ml. of base added is shown in Fig. 45.

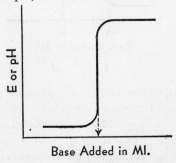

Base Added in Ml.

Fig. 45.

The end point corresponds to the intersection of the vertical portion of the curve with the x-axis.

A more sensitive means of detecting the end point is to plot $\frac{\Delta E}{\Delta ml.}$ versus ml. of base added (Fig. 46). The end point corresponds to the peak of the curve.

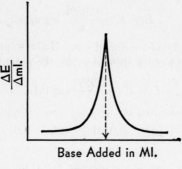

Base Added in Ml.

Fig. 46.

If the acid contains two replaceable hydrogen atoms, the neutralization usually proceeds in a stepwise manner and the plot of E versus ml. of base added (Fig. 47) shows an end point (i.e., a vertical portion

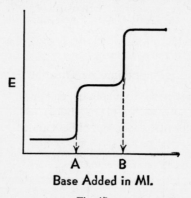

Base Added in Ml.

Fig. 47.

of the curve) corresponding to the neutralization of each hydrogen atom. Point A shows the ml. of base required to neutralize the first replaceable hydrogen, and point B indicates the ml. of base required to neutralize the second.

This method can also be used in the titration of oxidizing agents with reducing agents. In this case, E or $\Delta E/\Delta ml.$ is plotted versus ml. of reagent added. The usual experimental technique for oxidation-reduction reactions is to place a platinum electrode in the solution to be titrated and to combine it with a calomel electrode to form a complete cell. The potential is then determined after each addition of the reagent, and the end point is determined graphically as shown above.

Potentiometric titrations are especially useful in work with colored solutions for which the usual indicators would be useless.

Review Questions and Problems

1. With the aid of a diagram, describe the potentiometric method for the measurement of electromotive force.

2. With the aid of a diagram, describe the Weston standard cell.

3. Name and give examples of three types of reversible half-cells.

4. Derive:

$$E = E^0 - \frac{RT}{nF} \ln Q.$$

5. Calculate the potential of the following cell at 25° C. Write the cell reaction. Is the reaction spontaneous?

$$Pt;Cl_2;Cl^-{}_{(a=1)} \parallel Zn^{++}{}_{(a=1)};Zn.$$

6. Construct the cell which corresponds to the following reaction at 25° C.

$$Zn + Br_2 \rightarrow Zn^{++}{}_{(a=1)} + 2\ Br^-{}_{(a=1)}.$$

Calculate the potential of the cell. Is the reaction spontaneous?

7. Calculate K for the following reaction at 25° C.

$$Ag + Fe^{+++}{}_{(a=1)} \rightarrow Ag^+{}_{(a=1)} + Fe^{++}.$$

What would be the potential of the cell if the activity of Ag^+ were 0.1 instead of 1?

8. Given the following cell at 25° C.:

$$Pt;X_2;X^-{}_{(a=0.1)} \parallel X^-{}_{(a=0.01)};X_2;Pt,$$

in which X_2 is some unspecified nonmetal:

    (a) Write the cell reaction.
    (b) Calculate E and ΔF.
    (c) Is the reaction spontaneous?

9. For a certain solution $a_{H+} = 3 \times 10^{-4}$. Calculate the pH.

13

Ionic Equilibria

Equilibria involving ions in solution will be discussed in this chapter. The reader should review elementary material on the topic before studying this section.

Ionization of Weak Electrolytes

The Arrhenius theory of electrolytic dissociation is applicable to solutions of weak acids and weak bases. For example, in a solution of acetic acid, HAc, the following equilibrium exists between the undissociated molecules and the ions:

$$CH_3COOH \rightleftarrows H^+ + CH_3COO^-$$

or:
$$HAc \rightleftarrows H^+ + Ac^-.$$

It can be shown that:

$$\alpha = \frac{\Lambda}{\Lambda_0}, \qquad\qquad 13:1$$

in which: α = degree of dissociation,
Λ = equivalent conductance of the solution,
Λ_0 = equivalent conductance of the solution at infinite dilution.

Ionization Constants

The ionization constant is the equilibrium constant for an ionic equilibrium. If the ionization of an acid is under consideration the symbol K_a is used; if the ionization of a base is under consideration the symbol K_b is used. For example, in the ionization of acetic acid:

$$K_a = \frac{[H^+][Ac^-]}{[HAc]},$$

138

in which: $[H^+]$ = equilibrium concentration of H^+ in moles per liter,
$[Ac^-]$ = equilibrium concentration of Ac^- in moles per liter,
$[HAc]$ = equilibrium concentration of HAc in moles per liter.

However: $[H^+] = \alpha c,$
$[Ac^-] = \alpha c,$
$[HAc] = (1 - \alpha)c,$

in which: α = degree of dissociation,
c = original concentration of acetic acid.

Note. It is assumed that solutions considered in this chapter are sufficiently dilute to permit the use of concentrations in place of activities.

Then:
$$K_a = \frac{(\alpha c)(\alpha c)}{(1 - \alpha)c} = \frac{\alpha^2 c}{1 - \alpha}.$$

For most weak electrolytes, α is small and $1 - \alpha \cong 1$, and:

$$K_a = \alpha^2 c.$$

Example. For a 0.0128 normal solution of acetic acid at 25° C., $\Lambda = 14.4$ mhos/equivalent. $\Lambda_0 = 391$ mhos/equivalent. Calculate K_a.

$$\alpha = \frac{\Lambda}{\Lambda_0} = \frac{14.4}{391} = 0.0368.$$
$$K_a = \frac{\alpha^2 c}{1 - \alpha} = \frac{(0.0368)^2(0.0128)}{(1 - 0.0368)}.$$
$$= 1.80 \times 10^{-5}$$

or: $\qquad K_a = \alpha^2 c = 1.73 \times 10^{-5}$

Polybasic acids ionize in a stepwise manner. For H_2S the equilibria are:

$$H_2S \rightleftarrows H^+ + HS^-,$$
$$HS^- \rightleftarrows H^+ + S^=.$$

Thus there are two ionization constants involved, K_1 for the first step and K_2 for the second step. At 25° C.:

$$K_1 = \frac{[H^+][HS^-]}{[H_2S]} = 9.1 \times 10^{-8}.$$
$$K_2 = \frac{[H^+][S^=]}{[HS^-]} = 1.2 \times 10^{-15}.$$

In general K_1 is so much greater than K_2 that $[H^+]$ is derived almost entirely from the primary ionization.

The values of K_a and K_b for several acids and bases at 25° C. are given in Table 12 (p. 140).

TABLE 12

IONIZATION CONSTANTS

Substance	Formula	K_{Ion}
Trichloroacetic acid	Cl_3CCOOH	2×10^{-1}
Dichloroacetic acid	$Cl_2CHCOOH$	5.2×10^{-2}
Monochloroacetic acid	$ClCH_2COOH$	1.38×10^{-3}
Acetic acid	CH_3COOH	1.8×10^{-5}
Hydrocyanic acid	HCN	7.2×10^{-10}
Benzoic acid	C_6H_5COOH	6.6×10^{-5}
Methylamine	CH_3NH_2	4.0×10^{-4}
Ammonium hydroxide	NH_4OH	1.8×10^{-5}

The Common Ion Effect

If to a solution of a weak acid HA, a substance is added which possesses an ion in common with the acid (e.g., HCl or the salt NaA), the degree of dissociation is repressed, as would be expected from Le Châtelier's principle.

Example. Calculate α at 25° C. for (a) a 0.1-molar solution of HAc and (b) a 0.1-molar solution of HAc which is 0.2-molar with respect to NaAc.

$$\text{(a)} \quad K_a = \alpha^2 c.$$
$$1.8 \times 10^{-5} = 0.1\alpha^2.$$
$$\alpha = \sqrt{1.8 \times 10^{-4}}$$
$$= \sqrt{1.8} \times 10^{-2} = 1.34 \times 10^{-2}.$$

$$\text{(b)} \quad HAc \rightleftarrows H^+ + Ac^-.$$
$$NaAc \rightarrow Na^+ + Ac^-.$$

Sodium acetate is a salt and may be assumed to be completely dissociated in solution.

$$K_a = \frac{[H^+][Ac^-]}{[HAc]}.$$
$$[H^+] = \alpha c = 0.1\alpha.$$
$$[Ac^-] = \alpha c + 0.200 \cong 0.2 \quad \text{since } \alpha \text{ is very small.}$$
$$[HAc] = 0.1(1 - \alpha) \cong 0.1 \quad \text{since } \alpha \text{ is very small.}$$
$$1.8 \times 10^{-5} = (0.1\alpha)(0.2)/0.1.$$
$$\alpha = 9.00 \times 10^{-5}.$$

Ion Product of Water

Water slightly ionizes according to the following equation:

$$H_2O \rightleftarrows H^+ + OH^-,$$

and the ionization constant is:

$$K_{ion} = \frac{[H^+][OH^-]}{[H_2O]}.$$

It is found from conductance measurements that for water at $25°$ C.:

$$\Lambda = 9.9 \times 10^{-7} \text{ mhos/equivalent},$$
$$\Lambda_0 = l_c + l_a = 547.8 \text{ mhos/equivalent}.$$

Then:

$$\alpha = \frac{\Lambda}{\Lambda_0} = \frac{9.9 \times 10^{-7}}{547.8} = 1.81 \times 10^{-9}.$$

Since one liter of water contains $\frac{1000}{18.0}$ or 55.5 moles and since:

$$[H^+] = [OH^-] = \alpha c = (1.8 \times 10^{-9})(55.5) = 1.00 \times 10^{-7},$$

then:

$$K_{ion} = \frac{(1.00 \times 10^{-7})(1.00 \times 10^{-7})}{55.5} = 1.8 \times 10^{-16}.$$

Since the $[H_2O]$ is essentially constant:

$$K_w = K_{ion}[H_2O] = [H^+][OH^-]. \qquad \textbf{13:2}$$
$$K_w = (1.00 \times 10^{-7})(1.00 \times 10^{-7}) = 1.00 \times 10^{-14},$$

in which K_w is a constant called the *ion product of water*. Thus, in pure water or in any dilute aqueous solution at $25°$ C., the product of the concentrations of the hydrogen and hydroxyl ions is 1.00×10^{-14}.

Hydrolysis

Hydrolysis is the reaction between a salt and water to yield an acid and a base. Four cases can be distinguished in considering the hydrolytic behavior of salts:

1. The salts of strong acids and strong bases (e.g., NaCl) do not undergo hydrolysis.

2. The salts of weak acids and strong bases (e.g., NaAc) contain an anion which undergoes hydrolysis whereas the cation is unaffected. Representing such an anion as A^-:

$$A^- + H_2O \rightleftarrows HA + OH^-.$$

Thus the solution is basic as a result of the excess OH^-. The hydrolysis constant is:

$$K_h = \frac{[HA][OH^-]}{[A^-]},$$

or multiplying numerator and denominator by $[H^+]$:

$$K_h = \frac{[HA]}{[H^+][A^-]} \cdot [H^+][OH^-]$$

or:
$$K_h = \frac{K_w}{K_a},$$
13:3

in which: K_w = ion product of water,
K_a = ionization constant of the weak acid HA.

3. The salts of strong acids and weak bases (e.g., NH_4Cl) contain a cation which undergoes hydrolysis while the anion is unaffected. Representing such a cation as B^+, the following reaction occurs:

$$B^+ + H_2O \rightleftarrows BOH + H^+,$$

and the resulting solution is acidic. Then:

$$K_h = \frac{[BOH][H^+]}{[B^+]}.$$

Multiplying numerator and denominator by $[OH^-]$:

$$K_h = \frac{[BOH]}{[B^+][OH^-]} \cdot [H^+][OH^-]$$

or:
$$K_h = \frac{K_w}{K_b},$$
13:4

in which K_b = ionization constant of the weak base BOH.

4. The salts of weak acids and weak bases (e.g., NH_4Ac) contain a cation, B^+, and an anion, A^-, both of which are subject to hydrolysis:

$$B^+ + A^- + H_2O \rightleftarrows HA + BOH.$$

$$K_h = \frac{[HA][BOH]}{[B^+][A^-]}.$$

Multiplying numerator and denominator by $[H^+]$ and $[OH^-]$:

$$K_h = \frac{[HA]}{[H^+][A^-]} \cdot \frac{[BOH]}{[B^+][OH^-]} \cdot [H^+][OH^-]$$

or:
$$K_h = \frac{K_w}{K_a K_b}.$$
13:5

Example. Calculate the pH of a 0.1-molar solution of sodium acetate.

$$Ac^- + H_2O \rightleftharpoons HAc + OH^-.$$

$$K_a = 1.80 \times 10^{-5}.$$
$$K_w = 1.00 \times 10^{-14}.$$
$$K_h = \frac{K_w}{K_a} = \frac{\alpha^2 c}{1 - \alpha} \cong \alpha^2 c.$$
$$\frac{1.00 \times 10^{-14}}{1.80 \times 10^{-5}} = \alpha^2(0.1).$$
$$\alpha = 0.000075.$$
$$[OH^-] = \alpha c = (0.000075)(0.1) = 7.5 \times 10^{-6}.$$
$$[H^+] = \frac{K_w}{[OH^-]} = \frac{1.0 \times 10^{-14}}{7.5 \times 10^{-6}} = 1.33 \times 10^{-9}.$$
$$pH = -\log [H^+] = -\log 1.33 \times 10^{-9} = -[(0.124) + (-9)]$$
$$= 8.88.$$

Example. Show that for an aqueous solution of a salt of a weak base and a strong acid (such as NH_4Br):

$$pH = -\log \sqrt{\frac{K_w}{K_b} C_s},$$

in which C_s = concentration of the salt in moles/liter.

$$B^+ + H_2O \rightleftharpoons BOH + H^+.$$
$$K_h = \frac{K_w}{K_b} = \frac{[BOH][H^+]}{[B^+]}.$$
$$[B^+] = C_s.$$
$$[BOH] = [H^+].$$
$$\frac{K_w}{K_b} = \frac{[H^+]^2}{C_s}.$$
$$[H^+] = \sqrt{\frac{K_w}{K_b} C_s}.$$
$$pH = -\log [H^+] = -\log \sqrt{\frac{K_w}{K_b} C_s}.$$

Buffer Solutions

Solutions which resist changes in pH when acids or bases are added are called *buffer solutions*. Such solutions are usually composed of a weak acid and one of its salts or a weak base and one of its salts. Consider a buffer solution consisting of the weak acid HA and one of its salts BA. If a base is added to such a buffer solution, the base is neutralized by the acid:

$$OH^- + HA \rightleftharpoons H_2O + A^-.$$

If an acid is added, the H^+ reacts with the A^-:

$$H^+ + A^- \rightarrow HA.$$

Since:
$$K_a = \frac{[H^+][A^-]}{[HA]},$$

$$[H^+] = \frac{K_a[HA]}{[A^-]}.$$

As long as the amount of acid or base added is not large enough to change the ratio $[HA]/[A^-]$, the $[H^+]$ (and hence the pH) is constant.

Solubility Product

In dealing with saturated solutions of slightly soluble salts or metallic hydroxides, a special type of equilibrium constant called the *solubility product* is used. For example, for a saturated solution of $PbCl_2$ the following equilibrium exists:

$$PbCl_{2(s)} \rightleftarrows Pb^{++} + 2 Cl^-$$

and:
$$K_{sp} = [Pb^{++}][Cl^-]^2,$$

in which K_{sp} is the solubility product for $PbCl_2$. In general, for a saturated solution of any slightly soluble salt:

$$A_xB_{y(s)} \rightleftarrows xA^+ + yB^-,$$

$$K_{sp} = [A^+]^x[B^-]^y.$$

Example. The solubility of silver carbonate at 25° C. is 1.16×10^{-4} mole/liter. Calculate K_{sp}.

$$Ag_2CO_{3(s)} \rightleftarrows 2 Ag^+ + CO_3^=.$$

Since two silver ions are produced for each carbonate ion:

$$[Ag^+] = (2)(1.16 \times 10^{-4}) = 2.32 \times 10^{-4}.$$
$$[CO_3^=] = 1.16 \times 10^{-4}.$$
$$K_{sp} = [Ag^+]^2[CO_3^=] = (2.32 \times 10^{-4})^2(1.16 \times 10^{-4})$$
$$= 6.15 \times 10^{-12}.$$

Ionic Strength

The ionic strength, μ, of a solution is defined as:

$$\mu = \Sigma\tfrac{1}{2}mz^2 = \tfrac{1}{2}(m_1z_1^2 + m_2z_2^2 + m_3z_3^2 \cdots), \qquad \textbf{13:6}$$

in which m_1, m_2, m_3, $\cdots$ are the molalities of the various ions present and z_1, z_2, z_3, $\cdots$ are the valences of the respective ions.

Example. Calculate the ionic strength of:

     (a) 0.01-molal LiCl solution;

     (b) 0.001-molal $BaCl_2$ solution.

     (a) $\mu = \frac{1}{2}[(0.01)(1)^2 + (0.01)(1)^2] = 0.01.$

     (b) $\mu = \frac{1}{2}[(0.001)(2)^2 + (0.002)(1)^2] = 0.003.$

The ionic strength of a mixture is the sum of the ionic strength of the constituents. It has been established experimentally that in dilute solutions the mean activity coefficient of a given strong electrolyte is the same in all solutions of a given ionic strength.

The Interionic-Attraction Theory

As a result of the study of crystals of salts by X rays, it is now accepted that the units in the crystal lattice are ions. When a salt is dissolved in water the ions become free to move and conduct a current. Thus, a solution of a salt is to be regarded as 100% ionized. The decrease in equivalent conductance with an increase in concentration (Fig. 39) can be explained as a result of a decrease in ionic velocity as the concentration increases. This is the basis of the interionic-attraction theory of conductance.

According to this theory, at very high dilution the ions are so far apart that they have little effect upon each other. However, as the concentration is increased the ions come closer together and the attraction between ions of opposite charge causes a decrease in ionic velocities and hence a decrease in equivalent conductance. Debye, Hückel, and Onsager have developed these concepts quantitatively and derived the equation:

$$\Lambda = \Lambda_0 - (A + B\Lambda_0)\sqrt{c}, \qquad \textbf{13:7}$$

in which A and B are constants which depend on the solvent used and the temperature, and c is the normality. Thus according to the interionic-attraction theory a straight line should be obtained if Λ is plotted versus $\sqrt{c}$, which is the case as shown in Fig. 39.

It can be shown on the basis of the work required to separate ions in the process of dilution that:

$$\log \gamma = -Az_+z_-\sqrt{\mu},$$

in which γ = mean activity coefficient,

        A = constant for a given solvent at a given temperature, 0.509 for H_2O at 25° C.,

        z_+ = numerical value of the valence of positive ion,

        z_- = numerical value of the valence of negative ion,

        μ = ionic strength.

Example. Calculate the mean activity coefficient at 25° C. of (a) 0.01-molal solution of LiCl; (b) 0.001-molal solution of $BaCl_2$.

(a) $\log \gamma = -(0.509)(1)(1)\sqrt{0.01} = -0.0509.$
     $\gamma = 0.889.$

(b) $\log \gamma = -(0.509)(2)(1)\sqrt{0.003} = -0.0558.$
     $\gamma = 0.879.$

Proton Theory of Acids and Bases

According to the usual elementary definitions: (1) an acid is a substance which furnishes hydrogen ions in aqueous solutions, and (2) a base is a substance which furnishes hydroxyl ions in aqueous solutions.

A more general theory of acids and bases has been proposed by Brönsted and Lowry. According to this theory: (1) an acid is a substance with a tendency to lose a proton or H^+, and (2) a base is a substance with a tendency to gain a proton or H^+. Thus, if a substance loses a proton, the residue which is left must be a base:

$$A \;\rightarrow\; H^+ \;+\; B^-.$$
acid   proton   base

The acid and base which differ by a proton (as above) are said to form a *conjugate pair;* every acid must have its conjugate base and vice versa.

In order that an acid may exhibit its acidic properties (i.e., give up a proton), a base (i.e., a substance capable of accepting a proton) must be present. An example is the addition of acetic acid, HAc, to water:

$$HAc \;+\; H_2O \;\rightleftarrows\; H_3O^+ \;+\; Ac^-. \qquad \textbf{13:8}$$
acid₁   base₂   acid₂   base₁

The acetic acid donates a proton to the water molecule, which therefore acts as a base. Since the H_3O^+ can donate a proton to the Ac^- to reform HAc and H_2O, the H_3O^+ must be an acid and the Ac^- must be a base. Consequently any interaction of an acid and a base must produce a new acid and a new base. In equation 13:8 $acid_1$ and $base_1$ are conjugate pairs, as are $acid_2$ and $base_2$.

The following are examples of acid-base interactions in the Brönsted-Lowry sense:

$$Acid_1 \;+\; Base_2 \;\rightleftarrows\; Acid_2 \;+\; Base_1.$$
$$HCl \;+\; H_2O \;\rightleftarrows\; H_3O^+ \;+\; Cl^-.$$
$$HSO_4^- \;+\; H_2O \;\rightleftarrows\; H_3O^+ \;+\; SO_4^=.$$

$$H_2O \quad + \quad NH_3 \quad \rightleftarrows \quad NH_4^+ \quad + \quad OH^-.$$
$$H_2SO_3 \quad + \quad H_2O \quad \rightleftarrows \quad H_3O^+ \quad + \quad HSO_3^-.$$
$$HSO_3^- \quad + \quad H_2O \quad \rightleftarrows \quad H_3O^+ \quad + \quad SO_3^=.$$

Note that the acids and bases may be positive ions, negative ions, or neutral molecules. It can be seen that water can act either as an acid or as a base, i.e., water is *amphoteric*. It is important to note that in aqueous solutions of acids, a hydrated proton, H_3O^+, is obtained rather than the proton, H^+. H_3O^+ is called the *hydronium ion*.

The Brönsted-Lowry theory does not invalidate the equations previously derived in this chapter. Analogous equations can be derived in terms of this theory.

Review Questions and Problems

1. Explain the proton theory of acids and bases.

2. Derive an equation for the hydrogen ion concentration of a solution containing: (a) a weak acid and one of its salts; (b) a weak base and one of its salts.

3. Show that for a solution of H_2S, $[S^=] = K_2$.

4. A 0.100-molar solution of the acid HA is 1.00% ionized at 25° C. Calculate K_a. $HA \rightleftarrows H^+ + A^-$.

5. A 0.100-molar solution of the acid described in Problem 4 is also 0.2-molar with respect to the salt NaA. Calculate α and the pH of the solution. Assume $1 - \alpha \cong 1$.

6. At 25° C., the pH of a solution is 2.00. Calculate $[OH^-]$.

7. Calculate the pH of a 0.100-molar solution of NH_4Br at 25° C.

8. The solubility of a certain metallic hydroxide, $M(OH)_3$, is 1.00×10^{-5} mole/liter. Calculate K_{sp}.

9. Calculate the mean activity coefficient of a 0.001-molal solution of K_2SO_4.

14

Atomic and Nuclear Structure

The reader is advised to review elementary material on atomic structure and radioactivity.

The Electron

If a tube (Fig. 48) containing two electrodes is filled with a gas at a pressure of 10^{-2} mm. or less and an electric potential is applied across the electrodes, an electric discharge takes place and the negative electrode (cathode) emits a stream of rays (called *cathode rays*)

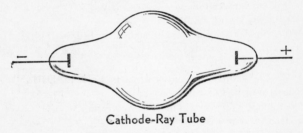

Cathode-Ray Tube

Fig. 48.

which move toward the anode. These rays: (1) travel in straight lines perpendicular to the cathode surface; (2) cause an opaque object placed in their path to cast a shadow; and (3) are deflected by electrical and magnetic fields in such a manner that they must bear a negative charge. These and other properties of cathode rays indicate that they are composed of negatively charged particles called *electrons*. That they are the same no matter what the source indicates they are constituents of all matter.

Behavior of Electrons in Electric and Magnetic Fields. Thomson studied the behavior of electrons in a combination of electric and magnetic fields. A beam of electrons was first subjected to an electric field of known strength. This caused a deflection of the beam. The amount of deflection is directly proportional to the charge of the electron and inversely proportional to its mass. A magnetic field was then applied perpendicular to the electric field. This field was of sufficient intensity to counterbalance the effect of the electric field. From a knowledge of the strengths of the electric and magnetic fields, it was possible to calculate the ratio of charge to mass for the electron, i.e., e/m, in which e is the charge on the electron and m is the mass of the electron.

Charge and Mass of the Electron. The charge on the electron can be determined by Millikan's oil-drop experiment. See Fig. 49. A droplet of oil is placed between two uncharged metal plates, and the rate of fall of the droplet under the influence of gravity is measured with the aid of a microscope. A beam of X rays is then admitted which causes some electrons to be detached from the gas molecules present. The oil droplet will then absorb one or more electrons and thus become negatively charged.

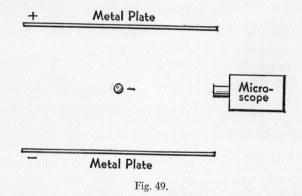

Fig. 49.

If the upper plate is now charged positively and the lower one negatively, the oil droplet will be attracted to the upper plate. If one electron is absorbed by the droplet, it will fall more slowly than it did under the influence of gravity alone. If a sufficient number of electrons are absorbed the droplet may even rise. The charge on the droplet at various times can be calculated from data on the changes in velocity of the oil drop as it absorbs one or more electrons. It is found that the charge on the droplet is either a certain minimum charge or an integral multiple thereof. This minimum charge is the charge on one electron, e, and is 1.60×10^{-19} coulombs. The charge on the electron is commonly represented as -1. Knowing e and using

e/m from Thomson's experiment, it is possible to calculate the mass of an electron:

$$m = \frac{e}{\dfrac{e}{m}} = 9.11 \times 10^{-28} \text{ grams}$$

or 1/1838 of the mass of a hydrogen atom.

The Proton

Positive rays are also present in the cathode-ray tube. They travel at high speeds toward the cathode. If the cathode is perforated they will pass through, and their behavior in electric and magnetic fields can be studied. The lightest particle found in this manner came from hydrogen. It has a mass of 1837/1838 that of a hydrogen atom and a charge of plus one. This particle, the proton, is the nucleus of the hydrogen atom.

The Neutron

In 1932 as a result of the study of the bombardment of beryllium by alpha particles (nuclei of helium atoms), Chadwick discovered a neutral particle which has a mass nearly equal to that of a proton. This particle is a neutron.

Isotopes and the Mass Spectrograph

Atoms which have the same atomic number but different atomic weights are isotopes. For example, chlorine consists of two isotopes; approximately 77% of the mixture is an isotope of atomic weight 35, and 23% is an isotope of atomic weight 37. This accounts for the observed atomic weight of 35.46.

The mass spectrograph is an instrument for the investigation of the isotopic composition of the elements. See Fig. 50. The positive rays

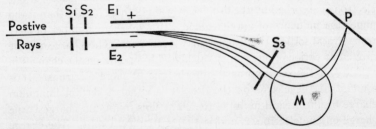

Fig. 50.

from a cathode-ray tube containing the element under investigation are passed through the slit systems, S_1 and S_2, and the resulting narrow beam is passed through the electric field applied across the plates E_1 and E_2. This causes the particles to be deflected downward; the amount of deflection depends on the mass and charge of the particle. Lighter particles are more easily deflected than heavier ones. The particles are thus separated into groups having a given ratio of charge to mass; only those particles which have a certain value for this ratio are passed by slit S_3. They then pass through the magnetic field M, which brings these particles to a focus at point P on the photographic plate. By suitable operation of the instrument a line will be found on development of the photographic plate for each isotope present, and by calibration of the instrument the masses of the isotopes can be determined. For example, if chlorine is analyzed, two lines are found corresponding to atomic weights 35 and 37, but no line is found at 35.46.

The isotopic composition of all the elements has been determined, and many elements have been found to consist of mixtures of isotopes.

The Nucleus

Alpha particles are the nuclei of helium atoms, i.e., they contain two neutrons and two protons. They are emitted by certain radioactive elements.

If a thin gold foil is bombarded by a stream of alpha particles, most of the alpha particles pass through unaffected. This proves that an atom is mostly empty space. However, a few alpha particles undergo a deflection of 90° or more. These deflections indicate that the gold atoms must possess small positive nuclei. The nucleus must be positive because it repels the positively charged alpha particles. The nucleus must be small because so few alpha particles are deflected. It is possible to calculate that in general the diameter of a nucleus is between 1/10,000 and 1/100,000 of the diameter of the atom as a whole.

The Atomic Number

If a metallic target is placed in a cathode-ray tube and bombarded with electrons, X rays are produced. They are electromagnetic waves of short wave length (about 10^{-8} cm.). Each metal (indeed, each element) emits X rays of its own characteristic wave length.

The wave length of the X rays emitted by an element is a function of the positive charge on the nucleus, and it is possible to calculate this positive charge from the observed wave length. This positive charge on the nucleus is called the *atomic number* and is equal to the number of protons in the nucleus.

Since the mass of the electron is negligible compared to the mass of the neutron and proton, it is clear that practically all the mass of the atom is concentrated in the nucleus, which contains neutrons and protons. If Z represents the atomic number and A represents the atomic weight, it follows that:

> the number of neutrons in the nucleus = $A - Z$;
> the number of protons in the nucleus = Z;
> the number of electrons in the atom   = Z.

Quantum Theory

In his studies of radiations from black bodies or perfect radiators, Planck was led to the hypothesis that black bodies radiate energy *discontinuously* in packets called *quanta*. This theory was generalized by Einstein, who suggested that *all* radiation is composed of quanta. The energy of a quantum is given by:

$$\epsilon = h\nu, \qquad\qquad \textbf{14:1}$$

in which: ϵ = energy of a quantum,
  h = Planck's constant = 6.624×10^{-27} erg-sec.,
  ν = frequency of radiation in sec.$^{-1}$.

This equation has been substantiated by experimental observation. The quantum theory is of special importance in the interpretation of atomic spectra.

The Line Spectra of Atoms

If a solid is heated to incandescence and the radiation passed through a spectrograph, a continuous spectrum is obtained. If a gas is heated to incandescence a series of lines (called *line spectra*) or bands (called *band spectra*) is obtained. Line spectra are emitted by atoms, and band spectra are emitted by molecules. Only line spectra are of interest here.

The simplest line spectrum is emitted by atomic hydrogen and consists of a number of lines which can be classified into several series. The wave lengths of lines in a given series can be calculated by the general formula:

$$\frac{1}{\lambda} = \overline{\nu} = R_H \left(\frac{1}{n_1^2} - \frac{1}{n_2^2} \right), \qquad\qquad \textbf{14:2}$$

in which: λ = wave length in cm. of a line in the series,
$\bar{\nu}$ = wave number = reciprocal of the wave length,
R_H = Rydberg constant for hydrogen = 109,677.76 cm.$^{-1}$.
n_1 = integer which is a constant for a given series,
n_2 = one in a series of integers the smallest of which is one greater than n_1. For example, if $n_1 = 1$, then $n_2 = 2,3,4,5 \cdots$.

In general the spectra of heavier elements can also be represented by similar series formulas.

Bohr's Theory of the Hydrogen Atom

In order to provide a theory of the atom capable of explaining the observed line spectrum for hydrogen, Bohr made the following postulates:

1. The electrons revolve in certain orbits or energy levels around the nucleus without radiating energy in the form of electromagnetic waves. The energy of an electron in an energy level is greater the farther the energy level is from the nucleus.

2. Electrons are restricted to energy levels in which their angular momentum is an integral multiple of $h/2\pi$, in which h is Planck's constant.

3. Each line in the spectrum of an element results from the fall of an electron from an energy level in which the energy of the electron is E_2 to an energy level closer to the nucleus in which its energy is E_1. As a result of such a fall a quantum of radiation of frequency ν is emitted in accordance with the equation:

$$E_2 - E_1 = h\nu, \qquad \textbf{14:3}$$

in which h is Planck's constant.

From these postulates, it is possible to derive the equation:

$$\bar{\nu} = \frac{2\pi^2 m e^4}{h^3 c}\left(\frac{1}{n_1^2} - \frac{1}{n_2^2}\right), \qquad \textbf{14:4}$$

in which: m = the mass of the electron,
e = the charge on the electron,
h = Planck's constant,
c = velocity of light.

This equation is obviously similar to equation 14:2, and if Bohr's assumptions are correct then:

$$R_H = \frac{2\pi^2 m e^4}{h^3 c}. \qquad \textbf{14:5}$$

If the known values of π, m, e, h, and c are substituted into equation
14:5, $R_H = 109{,}740$ cm.$^{-1}$, which is in good agreement with the experimental value of 109,678. This tends to confirm Bohr's postulates.

It is found that many spectral lines can be resolved into several
fine lines spaced close together. This can be explained on the basis
that an energy level may contain several sublevels. Thus when an
electron falls from an outer energy level to an inner energy level, it
may occupy one of several sublevels, which gives rise to several
closely spaced lines.

On the basis of spectroscopic evidence, it is possible to work out the
electron arrangement of the various atoms, much of which is already
familiar to the reader.

Wave Mechanics

Modern developments of the quantum theory (wave mechanics)
indicate that every particle is associated with a kind of periodic wave.
For example, the electron may exhibit wave properties (diffraction)
or particle properties (cast shadows). As a result of the wave-particle
nature of electrons, it is possible to calculate only the probability of
finding an electron at a given point. The wave mechanical theory of
atomic structure has superseded the Bohr theory, but in so doing it
has removed much of the concreteness of the Bohr model of the atom.

Radioactivity

Further insight into the nature of the nucleus of the atom can be
obtained from a study of radioactivity.

Becquerel in 1895 found that uranium compounds emit radiations
which can affect a photographic plate and cause the discharge of an
electroscope. The spontaneous emission of radiations by an element
is *radioactivity;* such elements are radioactive.

The Curies found that impure uranium ore was even more radioactive than pure uranium. This suggested that some impurity in the
ore was much more radioactive than uranium. From a large amount
of pitchblende (containing U_3O_8) they succeeded in isolating two new
radioactive elements, radium and polonium.

If some $RaCl_2$ is placed in a hollowed-out lead block (Fig. 51) and
the emitted rays are allowed to pass through an electric field, it is
found that they are split into three parts as shown. Each will cause a
darkening on the photographic plate, P, when it is developed.

It is found that the alpha particles (α particles) are attracted toward the negatively charged electrode, and further study of their

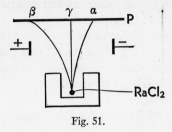

Fig. 51.

behavior shows them to be the nuclei of helium atoms, i.e., they consist of two protons and two neutrons. They are emitted with a velocity of about 0.1 the speed of light.

Beta particles (β particles) are deflected greatly toward the positively charged electrode, proving that they are negative. Their charge-to-mass ratio shows that they are electrons. They are emitted with velocities between 0.4 and 0.9 the velocity of light.

Gamma rays (γ rays) are not deflected by the electrical field. They are short-wave X rays which move with the speed of light and can penetrate thick sheets of metal.

The relative penetrating powers of α particles, β particles, and γ rays are roughly 1:100:10,000 respectively.

Theory of Radioactivity

According to the group-displacement law:

1. If an element emits an α particle, a new element is formed which differs from the parent element in having: (a) an atomic weight four units less; (b) an atomic number two units less; and (c) a place in the periodic table two places to the left of the parent element.

2. If an element emits a β particle, a new element is formed which differs from the parent element in having: (a) an atomic number one unit greater; and (b) a place in the periodic table one place to the right of the parent element. The atomic weights of the new and parent elements are the same.

The γ rays arise in certain cases as a result of energy rearrangements within the nucleus after emission of an α or β particle.

When radium spontaneously emits an α particle to form radon, the nuclear equation is:

$$_{88}\text{Ra}^{226} \rightarrow {}_{86}\text{Rn}^{222} + {}_2\text{He}^4.$$

The subscripts represent the charges on the nuclei (i.e., the atomic numbers), and the superscripts represent the atomic weights (mass numbers). The sum of the subscripts and superscripts must be the same on the two sides of the equation.

Three naturally radioactive series are known, which have $_{92}U^{238}$, $_{92}U^{235}$, and $_{90}Th^{232}$ as parent elements. These parent elements disintegrate in a series of steps by emission of α and β particles until finally a stable isotope of lead is formed.

Rate of Radioactive Disintegration

For a radioactive element:

$$-\frac{dN}{dt} = kN, \qquad\qquad \textbf{14:6}$$

in which: N = number of atoms present,

$-\dfrac{dN}{dt}$ = rate at which the number of atoms decreases,

k = rate constant which is characteristic of each radioactive element.

Integrating equation 14:6 between the limits $N = N_0$ at $t = 0$ and $N = N$ at $t = t$:

$$k = \frac{1}{t}\ln\frac{N_0}{N} = \frac{2.303}{t}\log\frac{N_0}{N}, \qquad\qquad \textbf{14:7}$$

and the half-life is:

$$t_{\frac{1}{2}} = \frac{0.693}{k}. \qquad\qquad \textbf{14:8}$$

The Positron

While studying the behavior of cosmic rays, Anderson in 1932 discovered a particle which is identical to the electron except that it has a positive charge. If the electron is represented as $_{-1}e^0$ (since the mass is negligible) the positron is $_{+1}e^0$.

Positrons may be produced by bombarding aluminum with α particles:

$$_{13}Al^{27} + {}_2He^4 \rightarrow {}_{15}P^{30} + {}_0n^1,$$
$$_{15}P^{30} \rightarrow {}_{14}Si^{30} + {}_{+1}e^0,$$

in which $_0n^1$ represents a neutron. The $_{15}P^{30}$ produced in the first step is artificially radioactive. It has a half-life of 2.55 minutes, emitting a positron as indicated.

Many artificially radioactive elements can be produced by bombarding appropriate target elements with high-speed α particles, protons, and deuterons (nuclei of heavy hydrogen atoms, i.e., a proton plus a neutron). The particles must be accelerated to high speeds in order to overcome the repulsion between the positively charged particle and the positively charged nucleus. These particles may be accelerated to suitably high speeds by means of a cyclotron. Most artificially radioactive elements emit electrons or positrons.

Artificially radioactive elements are useful because they can be traced through a series of chemical reactions by means of their radiations.

Generation of Neutrons

Neutrons may be produced by mixing beryllium and radium. The α particles emitted by the radium bombard the beryllium, producing neutrons:

$$_4Be^9 + {_2}He^4 \rightarrow {_6}C^{12} + {_0}n^1.$$

Neutrons are especially useful in initiating nuclear reactions since, being neutral, they are not repelled by positively charged target nuclei.

Energy and Mass

As a consequence of the theory of relativity, Einstein showed in 1906 that if matter is annihilated energy will appear in accordance with the equation:

$$E = mc^2, \qquad\qquad \textbf{14:9}$$

in which E = energy in ergs,

         m = mass in grams,

         c = velocity of light in cm./sec. = 3×10^{10} cm./sec.

This equation has been confirmed experimentally in measuring the masses and energies of reactants and products in nuclear reactions. Since the annihilation of a small amount of matter gives rise to such a large amount of energy, a feasible means of obtaining energy in this manner would obviously be desirable. This has been accomplished by means of nuclear fission. If $_{92}U^{235}$ is bombarded by slow neutrons, the nucleus undergoes fission as follows:

$$_0n^1 + {_{92}}U^{235} \rightarrow \text{two fission fragments plus one to three}$$
$$\text{neutrons plus energy.}$$

The fission fragments are isotopes of elements in the middle of the periodic table. In the process a relatively large amount of mass is consumed, which appears as energy in accordance with Einstein's equation. The neutrons produced can be used to keep the reaction going. This is an example of a chain reaction which is the basis of the atomic bomb.

The basis of the hydrogen bomb, on the other hand, is the fusion of various isotopes of hydrogen to form helium. A possible reaction is:

$$_1H^3 + {}_1H^2 \rightarrow {}_2He^4 + {}_0n^1 + \text{energy.}$$

This reaction is possible because the nuclei of elements in the middle of the periodic table are more stable than the nuclei of elements of high or low atomic number. Thus energy can be obtained as the result of the fusion of light nuclei as well as from the fission of heavy nuclei. These fusion reactions proceed only at very high temperatures, so that an atom bomb is needed to trigger a hydrogen bomb.

The cobalt bomb is a hydrogen bomb in a cobalt bomb case. The principle is that the cobalt becomes highly radioactive when disintegrated by the explosion, thus increasing the effectiveness of the hydrogen bomb.

Review Questions and Problems

1. What is a cathode-ray tube? Summarize the properties of cathode rays.

2. Explain the experiments by which the mass of an electron can be determined.

3. Explain the operation of the mass spectrograph.

4. What is the evidence that atoms have small positively charged nuclei?

5. What is the origin of the line spectra emitted by incandescent atoms?

6. Define radioactivity.

7. Define (a) alpha particles; (b) beta particles; (c) gamma rays.

8. Derive the formula for calculating the half-life of a radioactive element.

9. Complete the following nuclear equations:

$$_{11}Na^{23} + {}_2He^4 \rightarrow ? + {}_1H^1.$$
$$_{29}Cu^{64} \rightarrow {}_{28}Ni^{64} + ?$$
$$_4Be^9 + {}_1H^1 \rightarrow {}_3Li^6 + ?$$

10. In the Balmer series $n_1 = 2$ and $n_2 = 3, 4, 5 \cdots$ in equation 14:2. Calculate $\bar{\nu}$ for the first three lines in this series.

11. A certain radioactive element has a half-life of 1.00×10^{-6} sec. How long will it take for 90% of the element to disintegrate?

12. How much energy in ergs would be produced if one gram of $_{92}U^{235}$ were completely annihilated?

15

Molecular Structure

According to the electron theory of valence, the bonds which hold the atoms in a molecule together are related to the electron configurations of the atoms. Group 0 of the periodic table (Appendix VI) contains the inert gases which have the indicated electron configurations. The first through the sixth energy levels are known as the K, L, M, N, O, and P energy levels, respectively.

	K	L	M	N	O	P
He	2					
Ne	2	8				
A	2	8	8			
Kr	2	8	18	8		
Xe	2	8	18	18	8	
Rn	2	8	18	32	18	8

Since these gases are practically inert, it follows that an outer group of two electrons (in which case, only the first energy level is involved) or eight electrons (octet) constitutes an exceptionally stable arrangement. In general, atoms combine in such a manner as to attain an electron configuration like that of an inert gas (i.e., with eight or two electrons in their outer energy level). There are two ways in which this can be done: (1) by electron transfer (electrovalence), and (2) by sharing of electron pairs (covalence).

Electrovalence

A sodium atom can react with a fluorine atom (Fig. 52, p. 160) to form a sodium ion and a fluoride ion, each of which then has a complete octet. In the figure n represents a neutron, p represents a proton, and the electrons are represented by dots. For simplicity of notation, it is convenient to let the symbol of an element represent the atomic nucleus plus the electrons in the inner shells and to represent the electrons in the outer shell by dots, small circles, or x's. Then:

$$Na \cdot \ + \ \overset{\times\times}{\underset{\times\times}{\times F \times}} \ \rightarrow \ Na^{+1} \ + \ \overset{\times\times}{\underset{\times\times}{\vdots F \times^{-1}}}.$$

Elements in Group IIa of the periodic table have two electrons in the outer shell. They can react with two atoms of chlorine as follows:

$$Ca: \ + \ 2 \ \overset{\times\times}{\underset{\times\times}{\times Cl \times}} \ \rightarrow \ Ca^{+2} \ + \ 2 \ \overset{\times\times}{\underset{\times\times}{\vdots Cl \times^{-1}}}.$$

Solid electrovalent compounds consist of an interlocking lattice of positive and negative ions. In general, such compounds have high

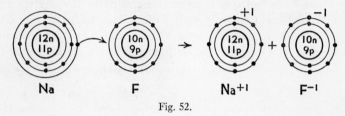

Fig. 52.

melting and boiling points, conduct an electric current when molten or dissolved in water, and are soluble in polar liquids (e.g., H_2O and C_2H_5OH) but insoluble in nonpolar liquids (e.g., CCl_4 and C_6H_6). Polar liquids are liquids with a dipole moment greater than zero. Nonpolar liquids are liquids with a dipole moment equal to zero.

Covalence

The energy required to remove an electron from an atom increases greatly with the number already removed. Hence ions with valences of three and four are rare. However, atoms can achieve an electron octet by the sharing of electrons in pairs. It can be shown by means of wave mechanics that a pair of electrons which have spins in opposite directions can be shared between two atoms to form a stable arrangement called a *covalent bond*. Several compounds involving covalent bonds follow:

A single line is used to represent a single covalent bond in the usual structural formulas. The above compounds would then be represented as:

$$Cl—Cl \qquad Cl—\overset{\displaystyle Cl}{\underset{\displaystyle Cl}{C}}—Cl \qquad H—\overset{\displaystyle}{\underset{\displaystyle H}{N}}—H$$

$$H—H \qquad H—Cl \qquad H—O—H$$

It is possible for atoms to share two or three pairs of electrons, e.g.:

$$H \quad H \\ \overset{\cdot\circ}{H}\overset{\circ}{:}C\overset{\times\circ}{:}\overset{\times}{C}\overset{\times}{:}H \qquad\qquad H\overset{\circ}{:}C\overset{:\times}{:}\overset{\times}{C}\overset{\circ}{:}H$$

$$H \quad H \\ H—C{=}C—H \qquad\qquad H—C{\equiv}C—H$$

in which each single line stands for the sharing of an electron pair.

Note that all atoms have complete octets (except hydrogen, which has a helium-like configuration). The tendency toward the octet is not universal; e.g., SF_6 is known, in which twelve electrons are found in the outermost energy level of the sulfur atom.

Covalent compounds ordinarily exist as single molecules in the solid state. In general they have low melting and boiling points, will not conduct an electric current in the liquid state nor when in solution, and are insoluble in polar solvents but soluble in nonpolar solvents.

According to modern ideas based on wave mechanics, all bonds have both electrovalent and covalent character, but usually one of these predominates.

Co-ordinate Covalence

In the covalent bonds considered in the previous section, each atom taking part in the formation of the covalent bond contributes one electron to the electron pair. If both electrons are supplied by one atom, a co-ordinate covalent bond is formed. For example, BF_3 reacts with NH_3 as follows:

$$\begin{array}{ccc} \overset{\times\times}{\times}F\overset{\times}{\times} & H & \overset{\times\times}{\times}F\overset{\times}{\times}H \\ \times\times \;\times\cdot & \cdot\circ & \times\times\;\times\cdot\;\;\cdot\circ \\ \times F\overset{\times}{\times}B & +\;\; :N\overset{\cdot}{:}H & \rightarrow \;\; \times F\overset{\times}{\times}B:N\overset{\cdot}{:}H \\ \times\times\;\cdot\times & \cdot\circ & \times\times\;\cdot\times\;\;\cdot\circ \\ \overset{\times}{\times}F\overset{\times}{\times} & H & \overset{\times}{\times}F\overset{\times}{\times}H \\ \times\times & & \times\times \end{array}$$

The bond between the boron and nitrogen atoms is a co-ordinate covalent bond. This is represented in structural formulas by an arrow pointing from the donor atom (i.e., the atom which donates the pair of electrons) to the acceptor atom. Then:

$$\begin{matrix} \text{F} & & \text{H} & & \text{F} & \text{H} \\ | & & | & & | & | \\ \text{F---B} & + & \text{N---H} & \rightarrow & \text{F---B} \leftarrow \text{N---H} \\ | & & | & & | & | \\ \text{F} & & \text{H} & & \text{F} & \text{H} \end{matrix}$$

In the reaction between ammonia and HCl, the proton from the HCl attaches itself to the "lone pair" of electrons in the NH_3 molecule:

$$\begin{matrix} \text{H} & & & & \text{H} \\ | & & & & | \\ \text{H---N:} & + & \text{HCl} & \rightarrow & \left[\text{H---N} \rightarrow \text{H} \right]^{+} \text{Cl}^{-} \\ | & & & & | \\ \text{H} & & & & \text{H} \end{matrix}$$

to give ammonium chloride, in which covalent bonds, a co-ordinate covalent bond, and an electrovalent bond are found.

Resonance

The concept of resonance is one of the most important applications of wave mechanics to molecular structure. If it is possible to represent the electronic structure of a molecule in two or more ways, in which the positions of the atomic nuclei are unchanged and in which the energies of the various structures are approximately the same, then the actual configuration of the molecule is a hybrid of the individual structures and the molecule has a stability greater than any of the individual structures. This phenomenon is called *resonance*. The interatomic distances are also shorter than would be expected. For example CO_2 can be represented by the following three structures:

$$\ddot{O}::C::\ddot{O} \quad ; \quad \ddot{O}::C:\ddot{O} \quad ; \quad \ddot{O}:::C:\ddot{O}$$

The middle structure is the O=C=O formula usually seen. However CO_2 is much more stable (or less reactive) than this formula would indicate. For example, CO_2 does not show the usual addition reactions of the C=O group as found in aldehydes. The explanation is that the actual structure is a hybrid of the above three forms and is more stable than any of them.

The remarkable stability of benzene is due to the fact that it is a hybrid of the following five structures:

As a result of resonance all carbon-to-carbon bonds in the molecule are identical.

The Hydrogen Bond

Under certain circumstances it is possible for the hydrogen atom in one molecule to be attracted by an unshared electron pair in another molecule, thus forming a bond between two atoms. An example is the HF_2^- in the KHF_2 which can be represented as $[FHF]^-$.

The atoms especially effective in forming such hydrogen bonds are fluorine, oxygen, and nitrogen. Other examples of hydrogen bonds (indicated by a dotted line) are:

Water:

$$\begin{array}{c} H \\ | \\ H-O\cdots\cdots H-O \\ | \\ H \end{array}$$

Alcohols:

$$\begin{array}{c} R \\ | \\ H-O\cdots\cdots H-O \\ | \\ R \end{array}$$

Carboxylic Acids:

$$R-C \underset{O-H\cdots\cdots O}{\overset{O\cdots\cdots H-O}{}} C-R$$

Thus water, alcohols, and carboxylic acids are associated molecules. These molecules have abnormal Trouton constants and Eötvös constants (Chapter 3). In the case of water and alcohols the hydrogen bonding can continue forming chains of indefinite length. Hydrogen bonding in the case of carboxylic acids results in the formation of a dimer. Hydrogen bonds are much weaker than ordinary bonds and are readily broken as the temperature is raised.

Review Questions and Problems

1. Explain with examples the meaning of electrovalence.

2. Explain with examples the meaning of covalence.

3. Summarize the main differences in the physical properties of electrovalent compounds and covalent compounds.

4. Explain with examples the meaning of co-ordinate covalence.

5. Using CO_2 and C_6H_6 as examples, explain the meaning of resonance.

6. Define hydrogen bond.   Illustrate.

7. Give electron formulas and structural formulas for: $HClO_4$, H_2SO_4, $CHCl_3$, NH_4Br.

16

Photochemistry

Photochemistry is the study of chemical reactions resulting from exposure of a system to radiation. The term *radiation* includes the whole electromagnetic spectrum ranging from high-frequency γ rays through X rays, ultraviolet rays, visible spectrum, and infrared rays to the low-frequency radio waves. However, radiations whose wave lengths lie between 2000 and 8000 Å. (i.e., the ultraviolet and visible region) are of special photochemical interest. Such reactions as combination, decomposition, polymerization, oxidation, and reduction can be brought about by photochemical means.

Ordinary chemical reactions are referred to as thermal or "dark" reactions in order to distinguish them from photochemical reactions. As explained in Chapter 6, all ordinary spontaneous reactions are accompanied by a decrease in free energy. However, certain photochemical reactions are accompanied by an increase in free energy as a result of the free energy supplied by the light. An example is the process of photosynthesis in which carbohydrates and oxygen are produced from carbon dioxide and water by the action of sunlight and chlorophyll.

Laws of Photochemistry

The amount of chemical change occurring in a photochemical reaction depends on the amount of radiation absorbed.

Grotthus-Draper Law. According to the Grotthus-Draper law, only that radiation which is absorbed can produce chemical change. However, absorbed radiation does not necessarily cause a chemical reaction. Absorbed radiation may simply be converted into heat, or it may be re-emitted as light of a different wave length. The latter phenomenon is called *fluorescence*.

Einstein's Law of the Photochemical Equivalent. According to Einstein's law of the photochemical equivalent, in the primary photochemical process a light-activated molecule absorbs one quantum of

165

radiation. Thus, for the primary process the number of molecules activated is equal to the number of quanta absorbed, and for a mole of 6.02×10^{23} molecules, a "mole of 6.02×10^{23} quanta" must be absorbed. A "mole of quanta" is called an *einstein*. The operation of the Einstein law is usually masked by secondary reactions or other complicating circumstances.

The quantum yield, Φ, is defined by the equation:

$$\Phi = \frac{\text{no. of molecules reacting}}{\text{no. of quanta absorbed}} = \frac{\text{no. of moles reacting}}{\text{no. of einsteins absorbed}}.$$

It is possible to draw conclusions regarding the mechanism of a reaction from the quantum yield.

Since the energy of one quantum is given by the equation:

$$\epsilon = h\nu \text{ ergs/quantum,}$$

in which:

$$h = \text{Planck's constant,}$$
$$\nu = \text{frequency,}$$

the energy per einstein, E, is:

$$E = Nh\nu \text{ ergs/mole,}$$

in which: $N = $ Avogadro's number.

Since: $\nu = \dfrac{c}{\lambda}$,

in which: $c = $ velocity of light $= 3.00 \times 10^{10}$ cm./sec.,
$\lambda = $ wave length in cm.,

then: $E = \dfrac{Nhc}{\lambda}$ ergs/mole

or: $E = \dfrac{Nhc}{4.184 \times 10^{7}\lambda}$ cal./mole. **16:1**

Substituting known values of N, h, and c into equation 16:1:

$$E = \frac{2.859}{\lambda} \text{ cal./mole.}$$

Example. For light of wave length 6000 Å., calculate ν, ϵ, and E.

$$\nu = \frac{c}{\lambda} = \frac{3.00 \times 10^{10}}{6000 \times 10^{-8}}$$
$$= 5.00 \times 10^{14} \text{ vibrations/sec.}$$
$$\epsilon = h\nu = (6.62 \times 10^{-27})(5.00 \times 10^{14})$$
$$= 3.31 \times 10^{-12} \text{ ergs/quantum.}$$
$$E = Nh\nu = (6.02 \times 10^{23})(3.31 \times 10^{-12})$$
$$= 1.99 \times 10^{12} \text{ ergs/mole.}$$
$$= \frac{2.859}{6000 \times 10^{-8}} = 4.765 \times 10^{4} \text{ cal./mole.}$$

Beer's Law

When dealing with solutions or gases, the intensity, I_a, of the absorbed radiation can be calculated from a form of Beer's law:

$$I_a = I_0(1 - e^{-kcl}) = I_0(1 - 10^{-\epsilon cl}),$$

in which I_0 = intensity of the incident radiation,

$e = 2.718$,

k = constant called the *absorption coefficient* which depends on the substance in question and the wave length of the radiation used,

c = concentration in moles/liter of the substance which absorbs the radiation,

l = length of the absorbing medium in cm.,

ϵ = constant called the *extinction coefficient*.

Most dilute solutions obey Beer's law, and it can be used for analytical purposes.

Experimental Procedure

The system under consideration is subjected to monochromatic radiation of the desired wave length. The number of moles of the light-absorbing substances that react in a given time can be determined by the usual analytical procedures. Glass vessels can be used in the visible-spectral range, but if ultraviolet light between 2000 and 3500 Å. is used, the vessels and other optical parts of the system must be made of quartz.

The Thermopile. The energy of the monochromatic radiation is measured by means of a thermopile, which is essentially a multi-junction thermocouple. The radiation falling on the thermopile is converted into heat, and the electric current produced is measured. Thermopiles can be calibrated with standard lamps available from the U.S. Bureau of Standards.

Measurements are made with and without the system under consideration placed between the light source and the thermopile. The difference gives the amount of radiation absorbed by the system.

The Actinometer. If extreme accuracy is not required, an actinometer may be used in place of a thermopile. An actinometer is a device for using a photochemical reaction to measure the amount of radiation absorbed by the system. For example, a dilute solution of oxalic acid containing some uranyl sulfate undergoes the following reaction when exposed to radiation between 2540 and 4350 Å.:

$$H_2C_2O_4 \xrightarrow{UO_2^{++}} H_2O + CO + CO_2.$$

The extent of decomposition (which can be measured by titration with permanganate) is a measure of the energy absorbed. This uranyl oxalate actinometer has been standardized for radiations of various wave lengths. The quantum yield, Φ, can then be calculated.

Example. For the photochemical reaction:

$$A \rightarrow B$$

it is found that 1.00×10^{-5} mole of B is formed as the result of the absorption of 6.00×10^7 ergs at 3600 Å. Calculate Φ.

$$\Phi = \frac{\text{no. of molecules reacting}}{\text{no. of quanta absorbed}}.$$

$$\text{No. of molecules reacting} = (1.00 \times 10^{-5})(6.02 \times 10^{23})$$
$$= 6.02 \times 10^{18}.$$

$$\text{No. of quanta absorbed} = \frac{\text{total energy absorbed}}{\text{energy of one quantum}}$$

$$= \frac{6.00 \times 10^7 \text{ ergs}}{h\nu}$$

$$= \frac{6.00 \times 10^7}{hc/\lambda}$$

$$= \frac{6.00 \times 10^7}{\dfrac{(6.62 \times 10^{-27})(3 \times 10^{10})}{3600 \times 10^{-8}}}$$

$$= 1.09 \times 10^{19}.$$

$$\Phi = \frac{6.02 \times 10^{18}}{1.09 \times 10^{19}} = 0.552.$$

Significance of Quantum Yields. The quantum yields and the approximate wave lengths (or range of wave lengths) of some photochemical reactions in the gaseous phase are given in Table 13.

TABLE 13

	Wave Length in Å.	Quantum Yield
1. $CH_3COOH \rightarrow CH_4 + CO_2$	<2300	1
2. $2 HI \rightarrow H_2 + I_2$	2800–3000	2
3. $H_2 + Cl_2 \rightarrow 2 HCl$	4000	about 10^5

Reaction 1 is an example of the quantum yield to be expected simply on the basis of Einstein's law. Reaction 2 proceeds by the following mechanism:

$$HI + h\nu \rightarrow H + I,$$
$$H + HI \rightarrow H_2 + I,$$
$$I + I \rightarrow I_2,$$

which gives two molecules reacting for each quantum absorbed. The first step is photochemical whereas the second and third steps represent thermal reactions.

Large quantum yields can be explained by means of a chain reaction. Reaction 3 proceeds as follows:

$$Cl_2 + h\nu \rightarrow 2\ Cl,$$
$$Cl + H_2 \rightarrow HCl + H,$$
$$H + Cl_2 \rightarrow HCl + Cl.$$

The first step is photochemical whereas the second and third steps are thermal reactions. The Cl atom produced in the third step allows steps 2 and 3 to be repeated indefinitely, accounting for the high quantum yield. However, the chain is finally broken by the reaction:

$$2\ Cl \rightarrow Cl_2$$

which takes place at the walls of the reaction vessel.

Low quantum yields are due to recombination of the products of the photochemical reaction or to deactivation of the light-absorbing molecule before it has time to react.

Photosensitized Reactions

Sometimes the reacting molecule is unable to absorb the radiation itself, but if a suitable atom or molecule (called a *sensitizer*) is present to absorb the radiation, it can then be passed on to the reacting molecule. Such a reaction is called a *photosensitized reaction*.

For example, hydrogen is not dissociated by ultraviolet light of 2537 Å. even though the energy corresponding to this radiation is more than the energy required to dissociate the H_2 molecule. However, if a small amount of mercury vapor is present, dissociation of the hydrogen takes place:

$$Hg + h\nu \rightarrow Hg^*,$$
$$Hg^* + H_2 \rightarrow Hg + 2\ H.$$

Hg represents a normal mercury atom, and Hg* represents an excited mercury atom. The hydrogen will readily reduce CO, C_2H_4, metallic oxides, and so on.

The uranyl ion acts as a sensitizer in the uranyl oxalate actinometer, and chlorophyll acts as a sensitizer in the process of photosynthesis.

Review Questions and Problems

1. State and explain the Grotthus-Draper law and the Einstein law of the photochemical equivalent.

2. Explain: (a) low quantum yields; (b) quantum yields equal to some small integer; (c) very high quantum yields.

3. Explain with examples what is meant by a photosensitized reaction.

4. Calculate the value of the einstein corresponding to radiation of wave length 4000 Å.

5. How many ergs of radiation of wave length 2500 Å. are required to decompose 0.001 mole of A in the reaction:

$$A \rightarrow 2B$$

if $\Phi = 2$ molecules/quantum?

17

Adsorption and Colloid Chemistry

Adsorption is the concentration of a substance at a surface. If the molecules of one phase actually penetrate among the molecules of the second phase more or less uniformly, the phenomenon is called *absorption*. For example, water is *absorbed* by a sponge, but acetic acid in solution is *adsorbed* by charcoal.

Adsorption

All solids tend to adsorb gases and solutes with which they are in contact. However, in order for the adsorption to be appreciable it is necessary that the adsorbent have a large surface area. For example, if charcoal is heated in steam or air, it is converted into a form which has a large surface area. Such charcoal is said to be *activated* and is widely used as an adsorbent. Other important adsorbents are silica gel, ZnO, Cr_2O_3, platinum, nickel, and copper.

Adsorption of Gases and Solutes by Solids. The amount of gas adsorbed by a solid depends on (1) the nature of the adsorbent, (2) the nature of the substance being adsorbed, (3) the surface area of the adsorbent, (4) the temperature, and (5) the pressure of the substance. A decrease in the temperature or an increase in the pressure increases the amount of adsorption.

Adsorption data can often be represented by the empirical equation of Freundlich:

$$y = kp^n, \hspace{4cm} \textbf{17:1}$$

in which: y = grams of substance adsorbed per gram of adsorbent,
  p = equilibrium pressure,
  k and n are constants which depend on the temperature.

A typical plot of the amount of adsorption as a function of pressure at constant temperature is shown in Fig. 53 (p. 172).

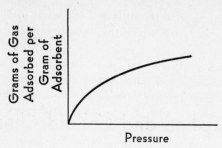

Fig. 53.

Such a plot is an *adsorption isotherm*.

Taking logarithms of both sides of equation 17:1:

$$\log y = n \log p + \log k.$$

If $\log y$ is plotted versus $\log p$ (Fig. 54) a straight line is obtained in which the slope is n. The Freundlich equation is satisfactory at low

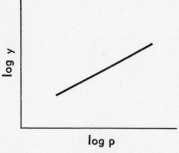

Fig. 54.

pressures, but at higher pressures, experimental data no longer fit the equation.

The Freundlich equation in the following form can be used to represent the adsorption of a solute by a solid (e.g., the adsorption of acetic acid by charcoal):

$$y = kc^n, \qquad\qquad\qquad \textbf{17:2}$$

in which: c = equilibrium concentration of the adsorbed substance,

             y, k, and n have the same significance as in equation 17:1.

The Langmuir Adsorption Isotherm. An adsorption equation of wide application has been derived by Langmuir, who postulated that: (1) the layer of gas molecules adsorbed by a solid is only one molecule thick; (2) the adsorption process consists of molecules condensing on and evaporating from the surface of the solid; and (3) an equilibrium is finally reached in which the rate of condensation equals the rate of evaporation.

Let θ = the fraction of a surface covered by molecules at a given instant. Then $1 - \theta$ = the fraction of the surface not covered by molecules and therefore available for adsorption. Then the rate of condensation is $k_1(1 - \theta)p$, in which k_1 is a constant and p is the pressure of the gas. Let k_2 represent the rate of evaporation from a surface of one square centimeter which is completely covered. Then for a partially covered surface, the rate of evaporation is $k_2\theta$.

Since at equilibrium the rate of condensation equals the rate of evaporation:

$$k_1(1 - \theta)p = k_2\theta.$$
$$k_1p - k_1\theta p = k_2\theta.$$
$$k_1p = k_2\theta + k_1\theta p.$$
$$k_1p = \theta(k_2 + k_1p).$$

$$\theta = \frac{k_1p}{k_2 + k_1p} = \frac{\dfrac{k_1}{k_2}p}{\dfrac{k_2}{k_2} + \dfrac{k_1}{k_2}p} = \frac{\dfrac{k_1}{k_2}p}{1 + \dfrac{k_1}{k_2}p}.$$

Let $b = k_1/k_2$; then:

$$\theta = \frac{bp}{1 + bp}.$$

The amount of gas adsorbed per gram of adsorbent, y, is proportional to the fraction of the surface covered, or:

$$y = k\theta = \frac{kbp}{1 + bp} = \frac{ap}{1 + bp}, \qquad \textbf{17:3}$$

in which: $\qquad\qquad k$ = a constant,
$$a = kb = \text{a constant.}$$

Equation 17:3 is known as the *Langmuir adsorption isotherm*. The values of a and b depend on the particular system under consideration and on the temperature. Dividing both sides of equation 17:3 by p:

$$\frac{y}{p} = \frac{a}{1 + bp}$$

or: $\qquad\qquad$
$$\frac{p}{y} = \frac{1 + bp}{a} = \frac{1}{a} + \frac{b}{a}p.$$

Thus a plot of p/y versus p should give a straight line. This is the case when experimental data are plotted over a relatively wide range of pressures.

Types of Adsorption. Two types of adsorption are known. The first type is *physical* or *van der Waals adsorption*, and is characterized by low heats of adsorption (about 5 or 10 kcal. per mole of gas). The forces responsible for this type of adsorption are believed to be the same as those that cause liquefaction and deviations of gases from ideal behavior.

The second type of adsorption is *chemical* or *activated adsorption* and is characterized by heats of adsorption between 10 and 100 kcal. per mole of gas. This is comparable in magnitude to the heat of formation of a chemical compound, and it is probable that, in chemical adsorption, there is a combination of gas molecules with surface atoms to form a surface compound. Physical adsorption is common at low temperatures, and chemical adsorption is common at high temperatures. Physical adsorption at low temperatures may pass into chemical adsorption as the temperature is raised.

The Gibbs Equation. The effect of concentration of a solute on the surface tension of a solution is given by the Gibbs equation:

$$u = -\frac{c}{RT}\frac{d\gamma}{dc}, \qquad\qquad 17:4$$

in which: u = excess concentration of solute in the surface layer per square cm. of surface (as compared to the concentration in the bulk of the solution),

c = concentration of solute in bulk of solution,

R = molar gas constant,

T = absolute temperature,

$\frac{d\gamma}{dc}$ = rate at which surface tension changes with concentration.

It follows that if γ decreases as the concentration increases (i.e., if $\frac{d\gamma}{dc}$ is negative), then u is positive and the solute must tend to concentrate in the surface layer. If γ increases with increasing concentration (i.e., if $\frac{d\gamma}{dc}$ is positive), then u is negative and therefore the surface concentration is less than the concentration in the bulk of the solution. Those solutes (e.g., soap) which concentrate in the surface layer have a large effect on surface phenomena and cause a great decrease in the surface tension. Those solutes (e.g., KCl) which concentrate in the bulk of the solution have little effect on surface phenomena and therefore can raise the surface tension only slightly.

Chromatographic Analysis. Chromatographic analysis uses the principle of selective adsorption combined with the fact that the rate of adsorption varies with a given adsorbent for different substances. Much of the work has been done on colored substances; hence the word "chromatographic."

The mixture to be separated is dissolved in a suitable solvent and passed through a column containing the adsorbent. The various substances are adsorbed consecutively, depending on the relative ease of adsorption. The most readily adsorbed substance is found in a band at the top of the column, and the least readily adsorbed substance is found in the lowest band. Since successive bands tend to overlap, pure solvent is poured through the column to desorb and readsorb each substance continually until a complete separation is effected. This process is called *elution*.

If a green leaf is extracted with petroleum ether and the extract is passed through a column of powdered sugar and properly eluted, the mixture can be separated into bands of color corresponding to the carotenes, chlorophyll A, chlorophyll B, and other colored compounds.

Monomolecular Films. If a small amount of a long-chain fatty acid (e.g., stearic acid, $C_{17}H_{35}COOH$) is dissolved in benzene and placed on the surface of pure water, the benzene will evaporate, leaving a film of acid on the surface of the water. This film will spread out to form a layer one molecule thick; such a film is called a *monolayer*. A long-chain fatty acid is made up of a polar end group (the carboxyl group) and a hydrocarbon residue. The polar end group is attracted by and dissolves in the water, and the insoluble hydrocarbon residue projects from the surface, as indicated in Fig. 55. This orientation

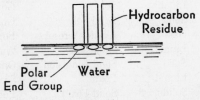

Fig. 55.

is also exhibited by higher alcohols and similar substances containing a polar end group.

The length and cross-sectional area of a single molecule of the monolayer of acid can be calculated as follows:

$$\text{Length of molecule} = \text{thickness of monolayer}$$
$$= \frac{\text{volume of acid}}{\text{area of monolayer}}.$$

$$\begin{aligned}\text{Cross-sectional area} \\ \text{of a single molecule}\end{aligned} = \frac{\text{area of monolayer}}{\text{no. of molecules of acid}}$$
$$= \frac{\text{area of monolayer}}{N \text{ (moles of acid)}},$$

in which: N = Avogadro's number.

The Colloidal State

A colloidal system consists of two phases, one of which is dispersed in the other. The dispersed phase is a discontinuous phase, and the dispersion medium is a continuous phase. The usual range of size of the dispersed particles is between 1 and 1000 mμ. (1 mμ. = 10^{-7} cm.) If the particles are larger than 1000 mμ. the system is a coarse suspension. If the particles are smaller than 1 mμ. the system is a true solution. The characteristic properties of the colloidal state are due to the large surface area of the dispersed phase. For example, a cube whose edge equals 1 cm. has a surface area of 6 sq. cm. If this cube is subdivided into small cubes that are 1 mμ. on edge, the total surface is 6000 sq. m. (about $1\frac{1}{2}$ acres).

Classification of Colloids. The classification of colloids is summarized in Table 14.

TABLE 14

Dispersed Phase	Dispersion Medium	Name	Example
Solid	Gas	Solid Aerosol	Smoke
Solid	Liquid	Sol	Gold in water
Solid	Solid	Solid Sol	Gold in glass
Liquid	Gas	Liquid Aerosol	Fog
Liquid	Liquid	Emulsion	Water in benzene
Liquid	Solid	Solid Emulsion	Opal
Gas	Liquid	Foam	Soap foam
Gas	Solid	Solid Foam	Pumice

Only sols and emulsions will be discussed in this book.

Sols. Sols are classified according to the liquid used as the dispersion medium. For example, water is the dispersion medium of a hydrosol, and alcohol is the dispersion medium of an alcosol. If the dispersion medium exerts an attraction on the dispersed phase the sol is said to be *lyophilic* (or *hydrophilic* if the dispersion medium is water). If there is little or no attraction between the dispersion medium and the dispersed phase the sol is *lyophobic* (or *hydrophobic* in the case of water).

PREPARATION OF SOLS. Since colloids represent a state of subdivision intermediate between a coarse suspension and a true solution, they may be prepared by dispersion of a coarse suspension or by condensation of particles in true solution.

Condensation Methods.

1. Double Decomposition. A sol of AgCl is produced if a very dilute $AgNO_3$ solution is added to a very dilute NaCl solution.

2. Oxidation or Reduction. A gold sol may be produced by reduction of $AuCl_3$ with formaldehyde.

3. Hydrolysis. A sol of hydrous ferric oxide, $Fe_2O_3 \cdot xH_2O$, is produced by hydrolysis when a concentrated ferric chloride solution is added dropwise to boiling water.

4. Change of Solvent. A sulfur sol may be produced through addition of water to a solution of sulfur in ethyl alcohol.

5. Arc Method. A copper sol may be prepared by striking an arc between two copper electrodes beneath the surface of water. The metal is vaporized and then condenses to a sol. Hydrosols of silver, gold, and platinum are readily obtained by this method.

Dispersion Methods.

1. Mechanical Disintegration. A practical device for the mechanical disintegration of coarse particles is the colloid mill. Two steel discs are placed close together and made to rotate rapidly in opposite directions. A coarse suspension is passed between the two discs, and as a result of the large shearing forces a sol is produced.

2. Peptization by Dispersion Medium. A substance is dispersed to particles of colloidal size by simple addition of the dispersion medium. The substance is said to be *peptized*, and the dispersion medium is the *peptizing agent*. For example, gelatin is peptized by water.

3. Peptization by Ions. Ions may also act as peptizing agents. For example, freshly precipitated AgCl is peptized by a solution containing the chloride ion.

PURIFICATION OF SOLS. A large excess of electrolyte may be present in a sol as a result of the method of preparation (e.g., double decomposition). This excess may cause coagulation upon standing and must be largely removed. A small amount of electrolyte is usually essential to the stability of a sol, and hence not all the excess electrolyte should be removed. The removal may be accomplished by dialysis or ultra-filtration.

Dialysis is the process of removing a dissolved substance from a colloid by means of a suitable membrane. Sol particles are not able to pass through a parchment (or similar) membrane whereas ions and other particles in true solution can. The sol is placed in a parchment sack which is immersed in a vessel containing water. The electrolyte diffuses from the sack, leaving the purified sol. The process may be hastened by use of an applied potential (electrodialysis).

Sols may also be purified by *ultrafiltration*. The sol is passed through a filter paper which has been impregnated with an appropriate substance such as collodion. The dispersion medium and electrolyte pass through, but the colloidal material remains. Pressure or suction is used to hasten the process. The colloidal material remains as a slime which is resuspended in pure media.

OPTICAL PROPERTIES OF SOLS. If a beam of light is passed through a true solution, the path of the beam through the solution is not visible. If a beam of light is passed through a sol, the beam is visible because of the scattering of the light by the colloidal particles. This is known as the *Tyndall effect*.

If a beam of light is brought to a focus within a colloidal solution and the image is viewed by means of a microscope at right angles to the path of the beam, the colloidal particles are seen as flashes of scattered light. Such an instrument is called an *ultramicroscope*. The apparent size of the reflections seen in the ultramicroscope bears no relation to the size of the particles. However, the ultramicroscope is valuable in determining the size of colloidal particles, as is shown in the following example.

Example. A certain mercury sol contained 0.020 g. of mercury per liter. When 10^{-9} ml. of sol was viewed in the ultramicroscope, 25 particles were observed. Assuming that the particles are spherical. calculate the average radius per particle. Density = 13.6.

$$\text{No. of particles per liter} = (25)\,\frac{10^3 \text{ ml./l.}}{10^{-9} \text{ ml.}}.$$

$$\text{Average mass per particle} = \frac{\text{Total mass}}{\text{No. of particles/l.}}$$

$$= \frac{0.020 \text{ g./l.}}{2.5 \times 10^{13} \text{ particles/l.}}$$

$$= 8 \times 10^{-16} \text{ g./particle.}$$

$$V = \frac{M}{D} = \frac{8 \times 10^{-16}}{13.6} = 5.88 \times 10^{-17}.$$

$$r^3 = \frac{3V}{4\pi} = 14.0 \times 10^{-18} \text{ cm}^3.$$

$$r = 2.41 \times 10^{-6} \text{ cm}.$$

Particles of colloidal size may be photographed with the *electron microscope*. The operation of this instrument is based on the fact that a beam of electrons under a constant voltage is similar to a beam of light. The beam of electrons may be focused by means of suitable magnetic fields just as a beam of light may be focused by means of glass lenses. It is possible to obtain photographs with a magnification of 100,000 diameters by means of the electron microscope.

KINETIC BEHAVIOR OF SOLS. Matter tends to diffuse from a region of high concentration to a region of low concentration. The diffusion constant, D, is the number of moles which diffuse across a unit area per unit time under a concentration gradient of unity. It can be shown that for spherical colloidal particles:

$$D = \frac{RT}{6N\pi\eta r}, \qquad \text{17:5}$$

in which:

D = diffusion constant,
R = molar gas constant,
T = absolute temperature,
N = Avogadro's number,
π = 3.14,
η = viscosity of the medium,
r = radius of the colloidal particles.

When particles are observed under the ultramicroscope, they are found to be in a state of ceaseless, random motion. This is due to the bombardment of the dispersed particles by molecules of the medium and is called *Brownian movement*. A typical plot of the positions of a colloidal particle at 30-second intervals is shown in Fig. 56.

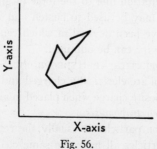

Fig. 56.

Einstein showed that:

$$D = \frac{\Delta^2}{2\,t},$$

in which Δ = average displacement produced by Brownian movement along the X-axis in time t.

Thus: $\Delta^2 = 2\,Dt = \dfrac{2\,RTt}{6\,N\pi\eta r} = \dfrac{RTt}{3\,N\pi\eta r}.$ **17:6**

Equation 17:6 can be used to determine the radius of a colloidal particle, or if this is known the equation can be used as a method for the evaluation of Avogadro's number.

SEDIMENTATION EQUILIBRIUM. The settling of colloidal particles is opposed by the Brownian movement, and finally a state of equilibrium is reached in which settling and diffusion balance each other. It can be shown that for particles of uniform size:

$$2.303 \log \frac{n_2}{n_1} = \frac{Nvg(d - d')(x_1 - x_2)}{RT},$$ **17:7**

in which the subscripts 1 and 2 refer to two different levels and:

n = number of particles at a particular level,
N = Avogadro's number,
R = molar gas constant in ergs/deg.-mole,
x = distance of particle from bottom of container in cm.,
g = acceleration due to gravity = 981 cm./sec.^{2},
d = density of particle,
d' = density of solvent,
T = absolute temperature,
v = volume of particle in cm.^{3}

Equation 17:7 can be used to determine the volume of colloidal particles. If the particles are spherical, the radius can be calculated.

Since the sedimentation due to the force of gravity is quite small, the ultracentrifuge may be used to hasten and increase the process. Ultracentrifuges have been devised in which centrifugal forces up to 4,000,000 times gravity can be obtained.

ELECTRICAL PROPERTIES OF HYDROPHOBIC SOLS. The particles of a hydrophobic sol are electrically charged and will migrate toward the electrode of opposite charge when placed in an electric field. This migration is called *electrophoresis*.

The charge on the particles is usually the result of adsorption of ions. Since the particles all have the same charge, they repel each other and precipitation is prevented. The ions adsorbed on the surface of the particles attract ions of opposite charge, leading to the formation of an electrical double layer. A simplified representation of the double layer is shown in Fig. 57 for a positively charged sol

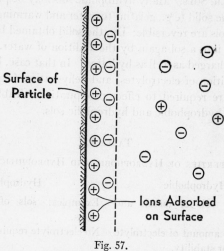

Surface of Particle

Ions Adsorbed on Surface

Fig. 57.

particle. Under the influence of an applied potential, the particle and a fixed film containing the ions between the particle surface and the dotted line move toward the negative electrode. The *zeta potential* is a potential drop which occurs between the dotted line in Fig. 57 and a point in the bulk of the solution. It has been shown that the stability of colloidal particles is a function of the zeta potential.

If the colloidal particles are not free to move and an electric potential is applied, the water will move. It will move with respect to the particles and in an opposite direction to that which they would normally take. This phenomenon is called *electroosmosis*.

PRECIPITATION OF SOLS. According to the Schulze-Hardy rule: (1) sols are precipitated by ions whose charge is opposite that of the sol particles, and (2) trivalent ions are much more effective in causing precipitation of a sol of opposite charge than divalent ions, which in turn are more effective than univalent ions.

Sols may be precipitated by adding an equivalent amount of a sol of opposite charge. For example, if a positive ferric oxide sol is added to a negative arsenious sulfide sol, mutual precipitation of both sols occurs.

A lyophilic sol, added to a lyophobic sol, often forms a coating around the particles of the lyophobic sol and renders them less sensitive to precipitation by electrolytes. An example is the addition of gelatin to a gold sol. The gelatin is then said to be a *protective colloid*.

HYDROPHILIC SOLS. Many hydrophilic sols may be prepared by the addition of the solid (e.g., gelatin) to water and warming. Ordinarily, hydrophilic sols are reversible; i.e., the solid obtained by evaporation can be made into a sol again by the addition of water. Hydrophilic sols may be charged as well as hydrated. In that case, both discharge (e.g., by addition of electrolytes) and dehydration (e.g., by addition of alcohol) are required to effect precipitation. Table 15 lists the properties of hydrophobic and hydrophilic sols.

TABLE 15

PROPERTIES OF HYDROPHOBIC AND HYDROPHILIC SOLS

Hydrophobic	Hydrophilic
1. Examples: sols of metals and salts.	Examples: sols of proteins and soaps.
2. Very small amount of electrolyte required for stability.	No electrolyte required for stability.
3. Precipitated by small amounts of electrolyte.	Not precipitated by small amounts of electrolyte.
4. Precipitation usually irreversible.	Precipitation usually reversible.
5. Viscosity about the same as water.	Viscosity higher than water.
6. Particles have a given electrical charge which is not easily changed.	Particles may be positive, negative, or neutral depending on pH.
7. Particles migrate under an applied potential.	Particles may or may not migrate under an applied potential.
8. Concentration of dispersed phase is low.	Concentration of dispersed phase can be high.

The pH at which a hydrophilic sol has no charge is called the *isoelectric point*. The stability is at a minimum at the isoelectric point.

Gels. Many hydrophilic sols will "set" under certain conditions to yield a semirigid, jelly-like solid which retains all the water. For example, a gel of gelatin is obtained by cooling a gelatin sol. It is believed that in the process of gel formation, the sol particles unite to form threads which become interlocked so that a semisolid form is produced. Most of the water is held between the threads by capillary forces.

Gels frequently shrink and exude liquid on standing. This is known as *syneresis*.

Some gels form sols when shaken and then revert to a gel on standing; this isothermal, reversible sol-gel transformation is called *thixotropy*.

Emulsions. An emulsion is a dispersion of one immiscible liquid in another. Ordinarily one of these liquids is water and the other is an oil. Thus two types of emulsions are possible: oil dispersed in water and water dispersed in oil. Water mixes readily with the oil-in-water type, and oil mixes readily with the water-in-oil type. This fact may be used to distinguish between the two types.

Emulsions are usually unstable unless a small amount of an appropriate emulsifying agent (e.g., soap or gelatin) is added. The emulsifying agent forms a film around the droplets and prevents their coalescence.

Emulsions may be prepared by means of a homogenizer in which the oil and water and emulsifying agent are forced through capillary tubes under high pressure and then allowed to impinge against a hard surface.

Emulsions may be broken by destruction of the emulsifying agent. For example, an emulsion in which sodium oleate is the emulsifying agent can be broken by adding an acid. This converts the sodium oleate to oleic acid, which has no emulsifying action. Heating, freezing, and centrifuging may also be employed in the breaking of emulsions.

Review Questions and Problems

1. Define adsorption. Give two forms of Freundlich's adsorption equation and define each symbol used.

2. Derive the Langmuir adsorption isotherm.

3. Distinguish between physical and chemical adsorption.

4. State the Gibbs equation and define each symbol used.

5. Describe four condensation methods and two dispersion methods for the preparation of sols.

6. Describe the purification of sols by: (a) dialysis; (b) electrodialysis; (c) ultrafiltration.

7. By means of a diagram show the nature of the electrical double layer at the surface of a negatively charged sol particle. Define zeta potential.

8. Explain how Avogadro's number can be determined from measurements based on the Brownian movement.

9. State the Schulze-Hardy rule.

10. State five differences between the properties of hydrophobic and hydrophilic sols.

11. How may the two types of emulsions be distinguished?

12. When 10^{-4} cm.^{3} of stearic acid (dissolved in benzene) is placed on the surface of water, a monolayer is formed which has an area of 400 cm.^{2} Calculate the length of a stearic acid molecule.

13. If each spherical particle in a mercury sol has a diameter of 100 mμ. and a density of 13.6, how many particles can be produced from 1.00 g. of mercury?

Appendixes

Appendix I

Answers to Problems

Chapter 2

6. $v = 179$ liters.

7. $M = 214$.

8. $\alpha = 0.200$.

9. $c = 4.61 \times 10^4$ cm./sec.

Chapter 3

4. $r = 0.0407$ cm.

6. $T_c = 516°$ K.

7. $\eta = 0.00495$ poise.

8. $T_c = 535°$ K.

74.1 cal./gram.

Chapter 4

4. $\lambda = 0.598$ Å.

5. Face-centered cubic.

Chapter 5

3. $\gamma = 32.2$ dynes/cm.

4. $R_m = 16.1$.

5. 229 g./l.

Chapter 6

14. $q = -7350$ cal.

$w = -703$ cal.

$\Delta E = -6650$ cal.

$\Delta H = -7350$ cal.

$\Delta F = 0$.

$\Delta A = 703$ cal.

$\Delta S = -20.8$ cal./deg.

15. $q = -514$ cal.

$w = -514$ cal.

$\Delta E = 0$.

$\Delta H = 0$.

$\Delta F = 514$ cal.

$\Delta A = 514$ cal.

$\Delta S = -1.38$ cal./deg.

16. $\Delta E = -336$ kcal.

17. $\Delta S = -0.875$ cal.

18. Efficiency = 55.7%.

19. $l = 46.4$ cal./gram.

20. $p = 659$ mm. = 0.867 atm.

21. $\Delta H = -213$ kcal.

Chapter 7

4. 1720 grams.

5. $p = 17.4$ mm.

6. B.P. = 100.037° C.

F.P. = $-0.136°$ C.

$\pi = 1.79$ atm.

7. $\pi = 5.68$ atm.

Chapter 8

6. $K_c = 1$.

$K_p = 0.00107$.

7. 0.124 mole.

8. $\Delta F^0 = 1070$ cal.

9. $K_p = 4.13 \times 10^{-4}$.

10. $K_p = 4/27\ P^3$

Chapter 10

7. $t_{\frac{1}{2}} = 15.9$ sec.

8. $t = 332$ sec.

9. (a) 100%.

(b) 75%.

(c) 67%.

10. $\Delta H_a = 19,400$ cal.

$k = 8.4 \times 10^{-5}$ liter/mole-min.

Chapter 11

5. $w = 0.0107$ g.

6. $\Lambda_0 = 389.5$ mhos/eq.

7. $\Lambda_0 = 39.7$ mhos/eq.

8. $n_c = 0.280$.

$n_a = 0.720$.

Chapter 12

5. $E^0 = -2.119$ volts.

$Zn^{++} + 2Cl^- \rightarrow Zn + Cl_2$.

Not spontaneous.

6. $Zn;Zn^{++}{}_{(a=1)} \parallel Br^-{}_{(a=1)};Br_2;$ Pt.

$E^0 = 1.827$ volts.

Spontaneous.

7. $K = 0.336$.

$E = 0.031$ volt.

8. (a) $X^-{}_{(a=.1)} \rightarrow X^-{}_{(a=.01)}$.

(b) $E = -0.0591$ volt.

$\Delta F = 1360$ cal.

(c) Not spontaneous.

9. pH $= 3.52$.

Chapter 13

4. $K_a = 1 \times 10^{-5}$.

5. $\alpha = 5 \times 10^{-5}$.

pH $= 5.30$.

6. $[OH^-] = 1 \times 10^{-12}$.

7. pH $= 5.13$.

8. $K_{sp} = 2.7 \times 10^{-19}$.

9. $\gamma = 0.879$.

Chapter 14

9. $_{12}Mg^{26}$.

$+_1e^0$.

$_2He^4$.

10. $\bar{\nu}$ (for $n_2 = 3$) $= 15{,}233.02$ cm.$^{-1}$

$\bar{\nu}$ (for $n_2 = 4$) $= 20{,}564.58$ cm.$^{-1}$

$\bar{\nu}$ (for $n_2 = 5$) $= 23{,}032.33$ cm.$^{-1}$

11. $t = 3.32 \times 10^{-6}$ sec.

12. $E = 9 \times 10^{20}$ ergs.

Chapter 15

7. (a)

(b)

(c)

(d)

Chapter 16

4. $E = 7.15 \times 10^4$ cal./mole.

5. 2.39×10^9 ergs.

Chapter 17

12. 25 Å.

13. 1.40×10^{14} particles.

Appendix II

Table of Physical Chemical Constants

Acceleration of gravity	981 cm./sec.^{2}
Molar volume (at 0° C. and 1 atm.)	22.4 liters
Avogadro's number	6.02×10^{23} mole^{-1}
Calorie	4.18 joules
Charge on electron	1.60×10^{-19} coulombs
Mass of electron	9.11×10^{-28} gram
Faraday	96,500 coulombs/gm.-equivalent
Planck's constant	6.62×10^{-27} erg-sec.
Velocity of light	3.00×10^{10} cm./sec.
Molar gas constant	8.31×10^7 ergs/deg.-mole
	8.31 joules/deg.-mole
	1.99 cal./deg.-mole
	0.0820 liter-atm./deg.-mole
Absolute zero	$-273°$ C.

The above approximate values should be used in the solution of problems in this book.

Appendix III

Greek Alphabet

Letters		Names	Letters		Names	Letters		Names
A	α	Alpha	I	ι	Iota	P	ρ	Rho
B	β	Beta	K	κ	Kappa	Σ	σ	Sigma
Γ	γ	Gamma	Λ	λ	Lambda	T	τ	Tau
Δ	δ	Delta	M	μ	Mu	Υ	υ	Upsilon
E	ϵ	Epsilon	N	ν	Nu	Φ	ϕ	Phi
Z	ζ	Zeta	Ξ	ξ	Xi	X	χ	Chi
H	η	Eta	O	o	Omicron	Ψ	ψ	Psi
Θ	θ	Theta	Π	π	Pi	Ω	ω	Omega

Appendix IV

Table of Logarithms

N	0	1	2	3	4	5	6	7	8	9	Proportional Parts				
											1	2	3	4	5
10	0000	0043	0086	0128	0170	0212	0253	0294	0334	0374	4	8	12	17	21
11	0414	0453	0492	0531	0569	0607	0645	0682	0719	0755	4	8	11	15	19
12	0792	0828	0864	0899	0934	0969	1004	1038	1072	1106	3	7	10	14	17
13	1139	1173	1206	1239	1271	1303	1335	1367	1399	1430	3	6	10	13	16
14	1461	1492	1523	1553	1584	1614	1644	1673	1703	1732	3	6	9	12	15
15	1761	1790	1818	1847	1875	1903	1931	1959	1987	2014	3	6	8	11	14
16	2041	2068	2095	2122	2148	2175	2201	2227	2253	2279	3	5	8	11	13
17	2304	2330	2355	2380	2405	2430	2455	2480	2504	2529	2	5	7	10	12
18	2553	2577	2601	2625	2648	2672	2695	2718	2742	2765	2	5	7	9	12
19	2788	2810	2833	2856	2878	2900	2923	2945	2967	2989	2	4	7	9	11
20	3010	3032	3054	3075	3096	3118	3139	3160	3181	3201	2	4	6	8	11
21	3222	3243	3263	3284	3304	3324	3345	3365	3385	3404	2	4	6	8	10
22	3424	3444	3464	3483	3502	3522	3541	3560	3579	3598	2	4	6	8	10
23	3617	3636	3655	3674	3692	3711	3729	3747	3766	3784	2	4	5	7	9
24	3802	3820	3838	3856	3874	3892	3909	3927	3945	3962	2	4	5	7	9
25	3979	3997	4014	4031	4048	4065	4082	4099	4116	4133	2	3	5	7	9
26	4150	4166	4183	4200	4216	4232	4249	4265	4281	4298	2	3	5	7	8
27	4314	4330	4346	4362	4378	4393	4409	4425	4440	4456	2	3	5	6	8
28	4472	4487	4502	4518	4533	4548	4564	4579	4594	4609	2	3	5	6	8
29	4624	4639	4654	4669	4683	4698	4713	4728	4742	4757	1	3	4	6	7
30	4771	4786	4800	4814	4829	4843	4857	4871	4886	4900	1	3	4	6	7
31	4914	4928	4942	4955	4969	4983	4997	5011	5024	5038	1	3	4	6	7
32	5051	5065	5079	5092	5105	5119	5132	5145	5159	5172	1	3	4	5	7
33	5185	5198	5211	5224	5237	5250	5263	5276	5289	5302	1	3	4	5	6
34	5315	5328	5340	5353	5366	5378	5391	5403	5416	5428	1	3	4	5	6
35	5441	5453	5465	5478	5490	5502	5514	5527	5539	5551	1	2	4	5	6
36	5563	5575	5587	5599	5611	5623	5635	5647	5658	5670	1	2	4	5	6
37	5682	5694	5705	5717	5729	5740	5752	5763	5775	5786	1	2	3	5	6
38	5798	5809	5821	5832	5843	5855	5866	5877	5888	5899	1	2	3	5	6
39	5911	5922	5933	5944	5955	5966	5977	5988	5999	6010	1	2	3	4	6
40	6021	6031	6042	6053	6064	6075	6085	6096	6107	6117	1	2	3	4	5
41	6128	6138	6149	6160	6170	6180	6191	6201	6212	6222	1	2	3	4	5
42	6232	6243	6253	6263	6274	6284	6294	6304	6314	6325	1	2	3	4	5
43	6335	6345	6355	6365	6375	6385	6395	6405	6415	6425	1	2	3	4	5
44	6435	6444	6454	6464	6474	6484	6493	6503	6513	6522	1	2	3	4	5
45	6532	6542	6551	6561	6571	6580	6590	6599	6609	6618	1	2	3	4	5
46	6628	6637	6646	6656	6665	6675	6684	6693	6702	6712	1	2	3	4	5
47	6721	6730	6739	6749	6758	6767	6776	6785	6794	6803	1	2	3	4	5
48	6812	6821	6830	6839	6848	6857	6866	6875	6884	6893	1	2	3	4	4
49	6902	6911	6920	6928	6937	6946	6955	6964	6972	6981	1	2	3	4	4
50	6990	6998	7007	7016	7024	7033	7042	7050	7059	7067	1	2	3	3	4
51	7076	7084	7093	7101	7110	7118	7126	7135	7143	7152	1	2	3	3	4
52	7160	7168	7177	7185	7193	7202	7210	7218	7226	7235	1	2	2	3	4
53	7243	7251	7259	7267	7275	7284	7292	7300	7308	7316	1	2	2	3	4
54	7324	7332	7340	7348	7356	7364	7372	7380	7388	7396	1	2	2	3	4
N	0	1	2	3	4	5	6	7	8	9	1	2	3	4	5

Table of Logarithms

(continued)

N	0	1	2	3	4	5	6	7	8	9	Proportional Parts				
											1	2	3	4	5
55	7404	7412	7419	7427	7435	7443	7451	7459	7466	7474	1	2	2	3	4
56	7482	7490	7497	7505	7513	7520	7528	7536	7543	7551	1	2	2	3	4
57	7559	7566	7574	7582	7589	7597	7604	7612	7619	7627	1	2	2	3	4
58	7634	7642	7649	7657	7664	7672	7679	7686	7694	7701	1	1	2	3	4
59	7709	7716	7723	7731	7738	7745	7752	7760	7767	7774	1	1	2	3	4
60	7782	7789	7796	7803	7810	7818	7825	7832	7839	7846	1	1	2	3	4
61	7853	7860	7868	7875	7882	7889	7896	7903	7910	7917	1	1	2	3	4
62	7924	7931	7938	7945	7952	7959	7966	7973	7980	7987	1	1	2	3	3
63	7993	8000	8007	8014	8021	8028	8035	8041	8048	8055	1	1	2	3	3
64	8062	8069	8075	8082	8089	8096	8102	8109	8116	8122	1	1	2	3	3
65	8129	8136	8142	8149	8156	8162	8169	8176	8182	8189	1	1	2	3	3
66	8195	8202	8209	8215	8222	8228	8235	8241	8248	8254	1	1	2	3	3
67	8261	8267	8274	8280	8287	8293	8299	8306	8312	8319	1	1	2	3	3
68	8325	8331	8338	8344	8351	8357	8363	8370	8376	8382	1	1	2	3	3
69	8388	8395	8401	8407	8414	8420	8426	8432	8439	8445	1	1	2	3	3
70	8451	8457	8463	8470	8476	8482	8488	8494	8500	8506	1	1	2	2	3
71	8513	8519	8525	8531	8537‘	8543	8549	8555	8561	8567	1	1	2	2	3
72	8573	8579	8585	8591	8597	8603	8609	8615	8621	8627	1	1	2	2	3
73	8633	8639	8645	8651	8657	8663	8669	8675	8681	8686	1	1	2	2	3
74	8692	8698	8704	8710	8716	8722	8727	8733	8739	8745	1	1	2	2	3
75	8751	8756	8762	8768	8774	8779	8785	8791	8797	8802	1	1	2	2	3
76	8808	8814	8820	8825	8831	8837	8842	8848	8854	8859	1	1	2	2	3
77	8865	8871	8876	8882	8887	8893	8899	8904	8910	8915	1	1	2	2	3
78	8921	8927	8932	8938	8943	8949	8954	8960	8965	8971	1	1	2	2	3
79	8976	8982	8987	8993	8998	9004	9009	9015	9020	9025	1	1	2	2	3
80	9031	9036	9042	9047	9053	9058	9063	9069	9074	9079	1	1	2	2	3
81	9085	9090	9096	9101	9106	9112	9117	9122	9128	9133	1	1	2	2	3
82	9138	9143	9149	9154	9159	9165	9170	9175	9180	9186	1	1	2	2	3
83	9191	9196	9201	9206	9212	9217	9222	9227	9232	9238	1	1	2	2	3
84	9243	9248	9253	9258	9263	9269	9274	9279	9284	9289	1	1	2	2	3
85	9294	9299	9304	9309	9315	9320	9325	9330	9335	9340	1	1	2	2	3
86	9345	9350	9355	9360	9365	9370	9375	9380	9385	9390	1	1	2	2	3
87	9395	9400	9405	9410	9415	9420	9425	9430	9435	9440	0	1	1	2	2
88	9445	9450	9455	9460	9465	9469	9474	9479	9484	9489	0	1	1	2	2
89	9494	9499	9504	9509	9513	9518	9523	9528	9533	9538	0	1	1	2	2
90	9542	9547	9552	9557	9562	9566	9571	9576	9581	9586	0	1	1	2	2
91	9590	9595	9600	9605	9609	9614	9619	9624	9628	9633	0	1	1	2	2
92	9638	9643	9647	9652	9657	9661	9666	9671	9675	9680	0	1	1	2	2
93	9685	9689	9694	9699	9703	9708	9713	9717	9722	9727	0	1	1	2	2
94	9731	9736	9741	9745	9750	9754	9759	9763	9768	9773	0	1	1	2	2
95	9777	9782	9786	9791	9795	9800	9805	9809	9814	9818	0	1	1	2	2
96	9823	9827	9832	9836	9841	9845	9850	9854	9859	9863	0	1	1	2	2
97	9868	9872	9877	9881	9886	9890	9894	9899	9903	9908	0	1	1	2	2
98	9912	9917	9921	9926	9930	9934	9939	9943	9948	9952	0	1	1	2	2
99	9956	9961	9965	9969	9974	9978	9983	9987	9991	9996	0	1	1	2	2
N	**0**	**1**	**2**	**3**	**4**	**5**	**6**	**7**	**8**	**9**	1	2	3	4	5

Appendix V

Table of International Atomic Weights (1953)*

Element	Symbol	Atomic No.	Atomic Weight	Element	Symbol	Atomic No.	Atomic Weight
Actinium	Ac	89	227	Neodymium	Nd	60	144.27
Aluminum	Al	13	26.98	Neon	Ne	10	20.183
Americium	Am	95	(243)	Neptunium	Np	93	(237)
Antimony	Sb	51	121.76	Nickel	Ni	28	58.69
Argon	A	18	39.944	Niobium	Nb	41	92.91
Arsenic	As	33	74.91	Nitrogen	N	7	14.008
Astatine	At	85	(210)	Osmium	Os	76	190.2
Barium	Ba	56	137.36	Oxygen	O	8	16.0000
Berkelium	Bk	97	(245)	Palladium	Pd	46	106.7
Beryllium	Be	4	9.013	Phosphorus	P	15	30.975
Bismuth	Bi	83	209.00	Platinum	Pt	78	195.23
Boron	B	5	10.82	Plutonium	Pu	94	(242)
Bromine	Br	35	79.916	Polonium	Po	84	210
Cadmium	Cd	48	112.41	Potassium	K	19	39.100
Calcium	Ca	20	40.08	Praseodymium	Pr	59	140.92
Californium	Cf	98	(246)	Promethium	Pm	61	(145)
Carbon	C	6	12.010	Protactinium	Pa	91	231
Cerium	Ce	58	140.13	Radium	Ra	88	226.05
Cesium	Cs	55	132.91	Radon	Rn	86	222
Chlorine	Cl	17	35.457	Rhenium	Re	75	186.31
Chromium	Cr	24	52.01	Rhodium	Rh	45	102.91
Cobalt	Co	27	58.94	Rubidium	Rb	37	85.48
Copper	Cu	29	63.54	Ruthenium	Ru	44	101.7
Curium	Cm	96	(243)	Samarium	Sm	62	150.43
Dysprosium	Dy	66	162.46	Scandium	Sc	21	44.96
Erbium	Er	68	167.2	Selenium	Se	34	78.96
Europium	Eu	63	152.0	Silicon	Si	14	28.09
Fluorine	F	9	19.00	Silver	Ag	47	107.880
Francium	Fr	87	(223)	Sodium	Na	11	22.997
Gadolinium	Gd	64	156.9	Strontium	Sr	38	87.63
Gallium	Ga	31	69.72	Sulfur	S	16	32.066
Germanium	Ge	32	72.60	Tantalum	Ta	73	180.88
Gold	Au	79	197.2	Technetium	Tc	43	(99)
Hafnium	Hf	72	178.6	Tellurium	Te	52	127.61
Helium	He	2	4.003	Terbium	Tb	65	159.2
Holmium	Ho	67	164.94	Thallium	Tl	81	204.39
Hydrogen	H	1	1.0080	Thorium	Th	90	232.12
Indium	In	49	114.76	Thulium	Tm	69	169.4
Iodine	I	53	126.91	Tin	Sn	50	118.70
Iridium	Ir	77	193.1	Titanium	Ti	22	47.90
Iron	Fe	26	55.85	Tungsten	W	74	183.92
Krypton	Kr	36	83.80	Uranium	U	92	238.07
Lanthanum	La	57	138.92	Vanadium	V	23	50.95
Lead	Pb	82	207.21	Xenon	Xe	54	131.3
Lithium	Li	3	6.940	Ytterbium	Yb	70	173.04
Lutecium	Lu	71	174.99	Yttrium	Y	39	88.92
Magnesium	Mg	12	24.32	Zinc	Zn	30	65.38
Manganese	Mn	25	54.93	Zirconium	Zr	40	91.22
Mercury	Hg	80	200.61				
Molybdenum	Mo	42	95.95				

* Values in parentheses denote the most stable known isotopes.

Appendix VI. The Periodic Table

Type of Hydride →		RH	RH_2	RH_3	RH_4	RH_3	RH_2	RH	
Type of Oxide →		R_2O	RO	R_2O_3	RO_2	R_2O_5	RO_3	R_2O_7	RO_4
PERIOD	GROUP 0	GROUP I	GROUP II	GROUP III	GROUP IV	GROUP V	GROUP VI	GROUP VII	GROUP VIII
0		1.008 **H** 1								
1	4.003 **He** 2	6.940 **Li** 3	9.02 **Be** 4	10.82 **B** 5	12.01 **C** 6	14.008 **N** 7	16.000 **O** 8	19.00 **F** 9	
2	20.183 **Ne** 10	22.997 **Na** 11	24.32 **Mg** 12	26.97 **Al** 13	28.06 **Si** 14	30.98 **P** 15	32.006 **S** 16	35.457 **Cl** 17	
3	39.944 **A** 18	(A) 39.096 **K** 19	(A) 40.08 **Ca** 20	(A) 45.10 **Sc** 21	(A) 47.90 **Ti** 22	(A) 50.95 **V** 23	(A) 52.01 **Cr** 24	(A) 54.93 **Mn** 25	55.85 **Fe** 26 — 58.94 **Co** 27 — 58.69 **Ni** 28
		(B) 63.54 **Cu** 29	(B) 65.38 **Zn** 30	(B) 69.72 **Ga** 31	(B) 72.60 **Ge** 32	(B) 74.91 **As** 33	(B) 78.96 **Se** 34	(B) 79.916 **Br** 35	
4	83.7 **Kr** 36	(A) 85.48 **Rb** 37	(A) 87.63 **Sr** 38	(A) 88.92 **Y** 39	(A) 91.22 **Zr** 40	(A) 92.91 **Cb** 41	(A) 95.95 **Mo** 42	(A) **Tc** 43	101.7 **Ru** 44 — 102.91 **Rh** 45 — 106.7 **Pd** 46
		(B) 107.880 **Ag** 47	(B) 112.41 **Cd** 48	(B) 114.76 **In** 49	(B) 118.70 **Sn** 50	(B) 121.76 **Sb** 51	(B) 127.61 **Te** 52	(B) 126.92 **I** 53	
5	131.3 **Xe** 54	(A) 132.91 **Cs** 55	(A) 137.36 **Ba** 56	(A) RARE-EARTH ELEMENTS 57-71	(A) 178.6 **Hf** 72	(A) 180.88 **Ta** 73	(A) 183.92 **W** 74	(A) 186.31 **Re** 75	190.2 **Os** 76 — 193.1 **Ir** 77 — 195.23 **Pt** 78
		(B) 197.2 **Au** 79	(B) 200.61 **Hg** 80	(B) 204.39 **Tl** 81	(B) 207.21 **Pb** 82	(B) 209.00 **Bi** 83	(B) **Po** 84	(B) **At** 85	
6	222. **Rn** 86	**Fr** 87	226.05 **Ra** 88	ACTINIDE SERIES 89-98					

RARE-EARTH ELEMENTS														
138.92 **La** 57	140.13 **Ce** 58	140.92 **Pr** 59	144.27 **Nd** 60	147.0 **Pm** 61	150.43 **Sm** 62	152.0 **Eu** 63	156.9 **Gd** 64	159.2 **Tb** 65	162.46 **Dy** 66	164.94 **Ho** 67	167.2 **Er** 68	169.4 **Tm** 69	173.04 **Yb** 70	175.0 **Lu** 71

ACTINIDE SERIES									
Ac 89	232.12 **Th** 90	231 **Pa** 91	238.07 **U** 92	**Np** 93	**Pu** 94	**Am** 95	**Cm** 96	**Bk** 97	**Cf** 98

Index

Index

A

Absolute temperature, 3
Absolute zero, 189
Absorption, 171
Absorption coefficient, 167
Absorption of heat, 42
Acids and bases, 146
  ionization constants of, 138–140
Actinometer, 167–168
Activated charcoal, 171
Activated complex, 109
Activated molecules, 107
Activation energy, 105, 107–108
Activity:
  of electrolytes, 126–127
  and equilibrium constant, 126
  and ionization constant, 138–139
  of ions, 126–127
  of liquids and solids, 127
Activity coefficient, 126
  and interionic attraction theory, 145
  and ionic strength, 145
Additive property, 36
  molar refraction as, 36
  parachor as, 38
Adiabatic expansion of a gas, 47
Adsorption, 171–176
  and absorption, 171
  activated, 174
  chemical, 174
  equation of, Gibbs, 174–175
  of gases, 171–174
  heat of, 174

isotherm:
  Freundlich, 171–172
  Langmuir, 172–174
  physical, 174
  of solutes, 171, 172
  and surface tension, 174
  and temperature, 171
  types of, 174
  van der Waals', 174
Aerosols, 176
Alpha particles, 151, 155
Ampere, 112
Amphoteric, 147
Angstrom unit, 31
Anions, equivalent conductance of, 119–120
Anisotropic crystals, 29
Anode, 113
Arrhenius:
  reaction rate equation, 105
  theory of electrolytic dissociation, 138
Association:
  of carboxylic acids, 163
  molecular, 11
  of water and alcohols, 163
Atomic:
  bomb, 158
  numbers, 151–152
  parachors, 38
  refraction, 36–37
  spectra, 152–153
  structure, 148–158
  weights, 192
Avogadro's hypothesis, 15

197

INDEX

205

Order of reflection, 33
Osmosis, 71
theories of, 72
Osmotic pressure, 71–72
Oxidation, 113, 123
electrolytic, 122
potentials, 130
and reduction titrations, 136–137

P

Parachor, 37–38
Partially miscible liquids, 95–96
Perfect gas, criteria for, 48
Perfect-gas law, 3–4
Periodic table, 193
Peptization, 177
Peptizing agent, 177
pH, 133–134
Phase, 86
Phase diagrams, 86–98
one-component systems, 86–90
sulfur, 88–90
water, 87–88
three-component systems, 96–98
two-component systems, 90–96
compound formation, 93–94
partial miscibility, 95–96
simple eutectic, 91–93
solid solutions, 94–95
Phase equilibria, 86–98
Phase rule, 86–98
Photochemistry, 165–170
laws of, 165–166
Photosensitized reactions, 169
Photosynthesis, 165, 169
Physical chemical constants, table of, 189
Physical chemistry, 1
Physical properties and molecular constitution, 36–40
Planck's constant, 152, 153, 166, 189
Poise, 26

Poiseuille's equation, 26
Poisons, catalytic, 110
Polar liquids, 160
Polar molecules, 39
Positive rays, 150
Positron, 156–157
Potential:
decomposition, 121
electrode, 123
junction, 124
measurement of, 124–125
standard electrode, 130
zeta, 181
Potentiometer, 124–125
Potentiometric titration, 135–137
Precipitation of sols, 181–182
Pressure, 3, 5
and chemical equilibrium, 79
critical, 16
gas, cause of, 12
in kinetic theory, 12–13
partial, 62–63
temperature diagram, 87
and transition point, 89
vapor, 21–23
variation of pv with, 6
and work of expansion, 43–44
Promoters, catalytic, 110
Protective colloid, 182
Proton, 150
theory of acids and bases, 146

Q

Quanta, 152
Quantum theory, 152, 154
Quantum yield, 166
significance of, 168–169

R

Radiation, 165
quantum theory of, 152